Transforming the Addictive Mind

Transforming the Addictive Mind

MBATT Book 1: The First Month of Mindfulness-Based Addiction & Trauma Therapy

Darrin Ford, M.A., LMFT, CSAT-S, MBATT-S & Christy Cosper, M.A., LMFT, CSAT

SANO PRESS

LONG BEACH, CA

Sano Press

Long Beach, ca

1st Edition (with minor edits 9/17/2020)

Book design, additional writing, and editing by **Chris Bordey**
Front Image Credit: Tumisu from Pixabay in accordance with Creative Commons CC0

ISBN 10: 0-692-93810-9
ISBN 13: 978-0-692-93810-2

Dedicated to the courageous people who have been willing to trust Mindful Centers with reclaiming their lives from the chaos of addictive behaviors.

TABLE OF

CONTENTS

Introduction

It was a warm summer day. I was eating lunch with a good friend. I was working at a psychiatric hospital, fresh out of school. As an intern, I was full of excitement, and this was my first job as a therapist. I felt like I was going to change the world! My duty was to work with emotionally disturbed children, and I believed it was up to me to heal them.

Perhaps you may already sense that this wouldn't work out well. During lunch, I suddenly felt as if I could not breathe. As I gasped for air, my friend sought a nurse or doctor but found none. She helped me to the car and raced back to the hospital. She grabbed the first psychiatrist we encountered and asked him to help me.

The psychiarist seemed amused when he said, "You're squeezing your water bottle very tightly." He looked at me for two seconds and declared, "There is nothing wrong. You are just having a panic attack." I was so relieved to hear him tell me what was happening.

I knew what a panic attack was from an academic perspective, but this was my first experience of it. Nothing could have prepared me for it. I was convinced I was going to die at any second. They took me to an ER where I was given medication to calm down. This was just the beginning. Over the next three months I became a prisoner in my own home. The walls of my home were my only place of safety. If I began to leave for any reason, I would begin having a panic attack all over. It became extremely difficult to leave the house, even to get to a doctor's appointment.

This experience was my first introduction to my mind. It took me three months of learning to recognize that the delusion my mind created was, in fact, just that: a *delusion*! From there, I confronted a myriad of delusions my mind had created and even entertained. They all had one common denominator, a motor running the show: addiction. It took me over ten years to become familiar with this concept.

Don't worry; it will not take you ten years. It will, however, take a good amount of time to see how addiction has deluded your ability to see reality. Addiction is an aversion to intimacy; one does not have the ability to experience vulnerability, for whatever reason, because the level of emotional discomfort is intolerable. In response, the mind defends itself by creating distractions from reality, and it does this through an addictive process.

To understand how your mind does this you must, as the famous Vietnamese Buddhist monk Thich Nhat Hanh once said, "Invite it in for tea." You must look closely at your delusional mind to stop the addictive process, and you will do just that through reading, writing, reflecting, meditating, and sharing with others your words to recovery.

With compassion and respect,

Darrin Ford
M.A., LMFT, CSAT, MBATT-S

How to Use This Book

Take it *one day at a time*. Do not try to rush through multiple days at once. For this workbook to be effective, each day should be thorougly completed in sequence. You should be in a comfortable, private setting when engaging this workbook. We strongly recommend going through this workbook with a trained Mindfulness-Based Addiction Therapist and be enrolled in group and individual therapy. This will ensure you get the most return for your time invested. **Each day is comprised of seven elements:**

1. *Ask the Addictive Mind* is a writing exercise that visits the thought process of you as an addict. It is encouraged that when you are writing as the addict, you use your non-dominate hand; if you are right-handed, use your left hand when writing as the addict. If you are left-handed, use your right. This process will be hard to do in the beginning. It will feel awkward, and the mind will easily be confused by it. That is a good thing! This means you are learning to think in a different way, which is exactly what we want. Why? The way

you currently think leads you to a destructive and emotionally painful place. If this were not the case, you would not be reading this.

2. *Feelings that Arose* and **Feedback Received.** For the first ten days, you will be asked to rate the intensity of eight different emotions that you may have experienced during *Ask the Addictive Mind.* For days 11 through 30, you will continue to rate the intensity of these emotions and write one to two sentences describing that emotion. The objective of these exercises is to build your awareness of feelings and to be able to *describe those feelings.* By building your emotional vocabulary and descriptive skills, you will improve your ability to express yourself honestly, which is vital for recovery.

Feedback Received requires that you read your writing exercises to a support group and/or individual therapist. This section may be done at a later time since group meetings and therapy sessions will vary. However, it is recommended that you do not go on to the next day until you have had a chance to share this work. When you do meet with your group and/or therapist to share, take notes of their feedback. It is important to review this feedback for any differences between what they hear you say and what you think you were conveying. Explore these differences with your trusted recovery group and therapist.

3. **The Antidote** is a reading that explores an alternative to the poison from *Ask the Addictive Mind.* The readings are varied and range from short stories to psycho-educational readings to autobiographical pieces from the authors.

4. *Meditation Exercise* follows *The Antidote* reading and involves sitting in silence with questions related to the topic of the day. If you have not meditated before, that is okay! In the beginning, it may be difficult or uncomfortable. The important thing is that you are willing and open to the process of meditation. Whether you have meditated before or not, it may be helpful to have someone read aloud the paragraph that begins "Notice your body..." as you sit still. For the first ten days, the meditation time is set to just 5 minutes, and as you progress through the workbook, the time will increase.

5. **New Mind Story** is a follow-up writing exercise in response to the reading and meditation. Only use your dominant hand. Unlike the first *Mind Story* which was a *dialogue* between two selves, this exercise is a *narrative* of your whole self.

6. **Feelings that Arose** and **Additional Feedback** repeats step two. This time, you will rate and describe the emotions that you may have experienced while completing the *Antidote* reading, meditation exercise, and *New Mind Story*. Share what you wrote for *New Mind Story* and the second *Feelings that Arose* with your recovery group and/or therapist. Take notes of their response to your share in *Additional Feedback*.

7. The end of each "day" concludes with two questions at the bottom of *Additional Feedback*. Briefly summariaze what you learned and name one thing you could do to care for yourself. You may write more than one thing down, but be realistic. In the beginning, it may be helpful to write one small thing that you know you will be able to carry out.

※

The first day will include directions for each section. If you are unsure with how to proceed on a worksheet, refer back to this section or review the directions included on day one.

Remember to take your time. Be honest with your process. You will only get as much out of this process as you put into it. You have already shown courage and capacity to heal. You are here reading this after all, beginning a journey towards healthy living. So remember,

be gentle with yourself.
Christy Cosper
M.A., LMFT, CSAT

The First 10 Days

5 MINUTES
MEDITATION

Directions: You are beginning a **dialogue** between yourself and the addictive mind. You are asking your addictive mind these questions. When responding as the addictive mind, use your non-dominate hand. As you write, you may have more questions or comments for the addictive mind. Write out these questions or thoughts with your dominant hand and respond with your non-dominant hand.

Today's date: Days sober:

Day 1 Poison: **Delusion**

Ask the addictive mind:

- When did I first meet you?

- Why are you here?

Mind's Story:

Feelings that arose

Directions: Reflect on what you were feeling and the intensity of those feelings as you completed *Ask the Addictive Mind*. Circle the corresponding number.

ANGER	1 UNNOTICABLE	2	3	4	5 FLOODED
FEAR	1 UNNOTICABLE	2	3	4	5 FLOODED
PAIN	1 UNNOTICABLE	2	3	4	5 FLOODED
JOY	1 UNNOTICABLE	2	3	4	5 FLOODED
PASSION	1 UNNOTICABLE	2	3	4	5 FLOODED
LOVE	1 UNNOTICABLE	2	3	4	5 FLOODED
SHAME	1 UNNOTICABLE	2	3	4	5 FLOODED
GUILT	1 UNNOTICABLE	2	3	4	5 FLOODED
OTHER:	1 UNNOTICABLE	2	3	4	5 FLOODED

Feedback received

Directions: We encourage you to see a Mindfulness-Based Addiction Therapist and attend group therapy to get the most out of these exercises. During individual and group therapy, share what you wrote in *Ask the Addictive Mind and Feelings that Arose*. On this page, take note of the group's (or your therapist's) feedback. This activity may not happen on the same day or week that you completed the worksheets, and that is okay. The important thing is that you practice vulnerability when you share what you have written. If you do not attend group therapy, you may skip this page.

Directions: Were there differences in how you rated your feelings and the feedback received in therapy? For example, did you rate Anger a '5' whereas group members sensed joy or guilt when you shared?

Discrepancies between *Feelings that Arose* and *Feedback Received?*

"We cannot solve our problems

Day 1 Antidote: *Open-Mindedness*

Ask yourself: Are you permanent? Many will quickly answer *Yes, I am permanent.* However, this is a delusion. No one or thing is permanent. All things are in transition. At the moment you are reading this, trillions of cells are working within your body. Your body is a process, not a completed project. It is a project *in motion.* As addicts, we love to focus on the destination. We think in terms of *this* or *that, good* or *bad, success* or *failure.* All of these concepts are delusional.

You are beginning a recovery practice, a process of lifelong discovery. That does not mean you will be in treatment for the rest of your life. Nor does it mean that emotional pain and strife you carry will always be. You will need to make lifestyle changes that cultivate intimacy with those around you, including yourself. In order to do so you must begin to shed the delusions of the addictive mind, and if you're reading this, you have already begun to open your mind to a new reality.

What is this new reality? In the past, addiction had control of your life, convincing you to follow a path to self-destruction. Cultivating a new reality means that you need to relinquish control and begin to trust

with the same thinking we used
when we created them."
—ALBERT EINSTEIN

in those further along the path of recovery than you currently are. Even when your addictive mind screams that they are wrong, you must trust in their words and follow through with what is asked of you.

Directions: Read through the gray box, then find a quiet space to sit uninterrupted in silence.

*E*xercise: To shed the delusions of the addictive mind one has to *look within*. **Sit in silence for 5 minutes.** Look within by asking yourself:

- How far am I willing to open my mind for a solid foundation in recovery?

- What good things can come from opening my mind?

££

Notice how your body feels as you sit with these questions. For example, what are you feeling in your shoulders? In your arms? In your legs and feet? What emotions arise within? What thoughts come into your awareness? Give labels to your responses. "Shoulder tension," "sadness," "thinking," "anger," "frustration." Once labeled, bring your attention back to your breathing. Notice the rhythm of your breathing. If you find your attention drifting to other thoughts, label those thoughts briefly and bring your attention back to your breath.

When you have completed your meditation, reflect on what you became aware of and write them down on the next page. Include the emotions you felt. Share your reflection with the group and take note of their feedback. There is no right or wrong way to do this. You just simply need to do it.

Today's date: Days sober:

Directions: Whereas the first *Mind Story* was a dialogue, *New Mind Story* is a narrative. Use only your dominant hand to reflect on the reading and meditation.

New Mind's Story:

Feelings that arose

Directions: Reflect on what you were feeling and the intensity of those feelings as you read *the Antidote*, meditated, and completed *New Mind Story*.

	1	2	3	4	5
ANGER	UNNOTICABLE				FLOODED
FEAR	UNNOTICABLE				FLOODED
PAIN	UNNOTICABLE				FLOODED
JOY	UNNOTICABLE				FLOODED
PASSION	UNNOTICABLE				FLOODED
LOVE	UNNOTICABLE				FLOODED
SHAME	UNNOTICABLE				FLOODED
GUILT	UNNOTICABLE				FLOODED
OTHER:	UNNOTICABLE				FLOODED

Additional feedback:

Directions: During group and/or individual therapy, share what you wrote in *New Mind Story* and the second *Feelings that Arose*. In this page, take note of the group's feedback. If you do not attend group therapy, you may skip this page.

Directions: At the end of each "day", write a summary of any insights you may have picked up. When listing one thing to care for yourself, list something you are sure you can do!

What I learned about myself today...

One thing I can do to care for myself tonight...

Today's date: Days sober:

Day 2 Poison: **Desire**

Ask the addictive mind:

- When would it have been enough?

- Could we sit with our desires and not act on them?

- Will I ever be free from your desires?

Mind's Story:

Feelings that arose

ANGER	1 UNNOTICABLE	2	3	4	5 FLOODED
FEAR	1 UNNOTICABLE	2	3	4	5 FLOODED
PAIN	1 UNNOTICABLE	2	3	4	5 FLOODED
JOY	1 UNNOTICABLE	2	3	4	5 FLOODED
PASSION	1 UNNOTICABLE	2	3	4	5 FLOODED
LOVE	1 UNNOTICABLE	2	3	4	5 FLOODED
SHAME	1 UNNOTICABLE	2	3	4	5 FLOODED
GUILT	1 UNNOTICABLE	2	3	4	5 FLOODED
OTHER:	1 UNNOTICABLE	2	3	4	5 FLOODED

Feedback received

Discrepancies between *Feelings that Arose* and *Feedback Received?*

"I want what I want when I

Day 2 Antidote: *Fulfillment*

Addiction is a demanding partner to have. It sees something it wants, and then the obsession begins. The addictive mind does a great job filling its desires and seizing all aspects of your life.

Don't let the addictive mind fool you; it will lead you down the same road every time. If you have a great day, you feel you are worthy of a reward and are entitled to act out. If the day was bad, you deserve redemption and act out. Fairly quickly the only focus in your life is acting out. Everything healthy and constructive fades away, and chaos floods in. If you are spending all your time, money and energy on obtaining *it*, participating in *it*, and covering up your trails, there is no time left to manage your life. Work is left unfinished, bills are left unpaid, obligations are forgotten, and lies spiral out of control. You begin to feel more stressed out, and are confused as to why your life feels so chaotic. The addictive mind thrives on these conditions and says, "See how stressed you are? You deserve to act out again, you've earned it!" As the cycle intensifies, implosion is inevitable. To break the cycle, the addict needs to find fulfillment.

want it, & I WANT IT RIGHT *now!*

—AMIG DELA

How do we get fulfillment? You need to:

- Nurture yourself

- Find healthy and loving connections with others

- Find healthy and loving behaviors

- Follow through with what is asked of you from recovery

- Find activities that bring you joy

- Create a loving relationship with yourself

In the past, the object of fulfillment for you has been the emptiness of addiction. Today you need to nurture healthy, loving connections and behaviors with others and self. Having a life of fulfillment in relationships and activities leaves no room for acting out. Your job now is to find the people and activities that bring you joy. Now go on and do it.

*E*xercise: To shed the delusions of the addictive mind, one has to *look within*. **Sit in silence for 5 minutes.** Look within by asking yourself:

- How can you cultivate true fulfillment in your life?

- What would a fulfilled life look like?

❧

Notice how your body feels as you sit with these questions. For example, what are you feeling in your shoulders? In your arms? In your legs and feet? What emotions arise within? What thoughts come into your awareness? Give labels to your responses. "Shoulder tension," "sadness," "thinking," "anger," "frustration." Once labeled, bring your attention back to your breathing. Notice the rhythm of your breathing. If you find your attention drifting to other thoughts, label those thoughts briefly and bring your attention back to your breath.

When you have completed your meditation, reflect on what you became aware of and write them down on the next page. Include the emotions you felt. Share your reflection with the group and take note of their feedback. There is no right or wrong way to do this. You just simply need to do it.

Today's date: Days sober:

*N*ew Mind's Story:

Feelings that arose

	1 UNNOTICABLE	2	3	4	5 FLOODED
ANGER	1	2	3	4	5
FEAR	1	2	3	4	5
PAIN	1	2	3	4	5
JOY	1	2	3	4	5
PASSION	1	2	3	4	5
LOVE	1	2	3	4	5
SHAME	1	2	3	4	5
GUILT	1	2	3	4	5
OTHER:	1	2	3	4	5

Each scale ranges from UNNOTICABLE (1) to FLOODED (5).

Today's date:

Additional feedback:

What I learned about myself today...

One thing I can do to care for myself tonight...

Today's date: Days sober:

Day 3 Poison: **Causes & Conditions**

Ask the addictive mind:

- What causes and conditions allow you to thrive?

- What clues do you leave before appearing?

- How can I get to know you and begin to understand what you are trying to tell me?

Mind's Story:

Feelings that arose

	1	2	3	4	5
ANGER	*UNNOTICABLE*				*FLOODED*
FEAR	*UNNOTICABLE*				*FLOODED*
PAIN	*UNNOTICABLE*				*FLOODED*
JOY	*UNNOTICABLE*				*FLOODED*
PASSION	*UNNOTICABLE*				*FLOODED*
LOVE	*UNNOTICABLE*				*FLOODED*
SHAME	*UNNOTICABLE*				*FLOODED*
GUILT	*UNNOTICABLE*				*FLOODED*
OTHER:	*UNNOTICABLE*				*FLOODED*

Feedback received

Discrepancies between *Feelings that Arose* and *Feedback Received?*

"Patience is bitter

Day 3 Antidote: *Patience*

As time passes, we as addicts in recovery develop a sense of pride and joy in our new found sobriety. We feel addiction is something we may be able to overcome. Around this time, we often form a story about those we love. We ask ourselves, our therapist, or group, "Why are they so upset? I am doing all the right things; can't they see that I am getting better?"

This "frustration" is our own unwillingness to accept our responsibility for the causes and conditions which left our loved ones emotionally pained. Perhaps we are unaware that our behaviors and actions have left them traumatized, our lies and deceptions have left them bewildered. Trust in the relationship is fractured. They are going through a mourning process; the person they thought you were is gone. They are still hesitant, afraid to embrace the person they now see.

We cannot shame ourselves for our betrayals. It is not constructive; it inhibits growth in recovery. To take responsibility, we have to completely acknowledge, without pretense, the magnitude of the pain we have caused others. The frustration we feel when we see the pain in our loved ones is not *them* causing it in us. It is a reflection of our own internal process.

but its fruit is sweet."

—JEAN-JACQUES ROUSSEAU

No one can make you feel anything. We are all responsible for our own mind states.

Recovery is a practice of patience. Mastery will not come in one day. Practicing patience involves being kind and gentle with those you have betrayed and with yourself. It is only through patience and practice that we can clean up the wreckage of our past. Being patient with those we love means we understand our actions have proved us untrustworthy at this time, regardless of where we are in recovery now. Patience is the key with them and ourselves.

*E*xercise: To shed the delusions of the addictive mind one has to *look within*. **Sit in silence for 5 minutes.** Look within by asking yourself:

- How can I practice patience with someone I love today?

- When I feel frustrated, what does that tell me?

- What is my part in all this?

❧

Notice how your body feels as you sit with these questions. For example, what are you feeling in your shoulders? In your arms? In your legs and feet? What emotions arise within? What thoughts come into your awareness? Give labels to your responses. "Shoulder tension," "sadness," "thinking," "anger," "frustration." Once labeled, bring your attention back to your breathing. Notice the rhythm of your breathing. If you find your attention drifting to other thoughts, label those thoughts briefly and bring your attention back to your breath.

When you have completed your meditation, reflect on what you became aware of and write them down on the next page. Include the emotions you felt. Share your reflection with the group and take note of their feedback. There is no right or wrong way to do this. You just simply need to do it.

Today's date: Days sober:

New Mind's Story:

Feelings that arose

	1 UNNOTICABLE	2	3	4	5 FLOODED
ANGER	1 UNNOTICABLE	2	3	4	5 FLOODED
FEAR	1 UNNOTICABLE	2	3	4	5 FLOODED
PAIN	1 UNNOTICABLE	2	3	4	5 FLOODED
JOY	1 UNNOTICABLE	2	3	4	5 FLOODED
PASSION	1 UNNOTICABLE	2	3	4	5 FLOODED
LOVE	1 UNNOTICABLE	2	3	4	5 FLOODED
SHAME	1 UNNOTICABLE	2	3	4	5 FLOODED
GUILT	1 UNNOTICABLE	2	3	4	5 FLOODED
OTHER:	1 UNNOTICABLE	2	3	4	5 FLOODED

Today's date:

Additional feedback:

What I learned about myself today...

One thing I can do to care for myself tonight...

Day 4 Poison: **Hidden Spots**

Ask the addictive mind:

- What ways might you begin to show yourself?

- How do I know when you are coming back to haunt me?

- Have you influenced any of my behaviors recently?

Mind's Story:

Feelings that arose

	1 UNNOTICABLE	2	3	4	5 FLOODED
ANGER	1 UNNOTICABLE	2	3	4	5 FLOODED
FEAR	1 UNNOTICABLE	2	3	4	5 FLOODED
PAIN	1 UNNOTICABLE	2	3	4	5 FLOODED
JOY	1 UNNOTICABLE	2	3	4	5 FLOODED
PASSION	1 UNNOTICABLE	2	3	4	5 FLOODED
LOVE	1 UNNOTICABLE	2	3	4	5 FLOODED
SHAME	1 UNNOTICABLE	2	3	4	5 FLOODED
GUILT	1 UNNOTICABLE	2	3	4	5 FLOODED
OTHER:	1 UNNOTICABLE	2	3	4	5 FLOODED

Feedback received

Discrepancies between *Feelings that Arose* and *Feedback Received?*

"The greatest barrier to some-

Day 4 Antidote: *Mindfulness*

The road ahead clears as time passes in recovery. A sense of reprieve and even a feeling of security may develop, but they are misleading. The addiction may not be active, but it still exists, waiting for a chance to return. Security and reprieve are denial in disguise. The addictive mind has been with us for years, possibly decades. At this early stage of recovery, we must remain vigilant.

Addiction is not limited to one area or period of our lives. The addictive mind expresses itself through other behaviors. If we have stopped acting out sexually, we may find ourselves drinking or shopping excessively or becoming a workaholic. Overdoing anything will throw you off balance, no matter what it is. Mindfulness is vital to preventing ourselves from spinning out of recovery, back down the road of addiction.

The way we increase our mindfulness is by focusing *mind* on reality versus what we hope or wish reality is. *Mind* is a sensory organ, and just as we focus the eye, we need to learn to focus the mind. When we work to become more aware, we are learning to see the thoughts of our mind without impulsively reacting to them. This takes time, consistency and repetition.

one achieving their potential is their denial of it." —SIMON TRAVAGLIA

Through the process of meditation, we are strengthening our ability to have awareness of our thoughts and not be reactionary to them. Consistently bringing mind back to breath increases our ability to align with what is real. If we are unable to be mindful, we are in reaction, impulse, and addiction. This is why daily meditation practice and mindfulness are the foundation for which we build all other aspects of our recovery. Through mindfulness, we become more intimate with ourselves which allows us to springboard into intimacy with others.

*E*xercise: To shed the delusions of the addictive mind one has to *look within*. **Sit in silence for 5 minutes.** Look within by asking yourself:

- Where is there risk for me?

- Am I doing anything out of the ordinary?

- Have my recent actions or responses been impulsive?

❧

Notice how your body feels as you sit with these questions. For example, what are you feeling in your shoulders? In your arms? In your legs and feet? What emotions arise within? What thoughts come into your awareness? Give labels to your responses. "Shoulder tension," "sadness," "thinking," "anger," "frustration." Once labeled, bring your attention back to your breathing. Notice the rhythm of your breathing. If you find your attention drifting to other thoughts, label those thoughts briefly and bring your attention back to your breath.

When you have completed your meditation, reflect on what you became aware of and write them down on the next page. Include the emotions you felt. Share your reflection with the group and take note of their feedback. There is no right or wrong way to do this. You just simply need to do it.

Today's date: Days sober:

*N*ew Mind's Story:

Feelings that arose

	1	2	3	4	5
ANGER	UNNOTICABLE				FLOODED
FEAR	UNNOTICABLE				FLOODED
PAIN	UNNOTICABLE				FLOODED
JOY	UNNOTICABLE				FLOODED
PASSION	UNNOTICABLE				FLOODED
LOVE	UNNOTICABLE				FLOODED
SHAME	UNNOTICABLE				FLOODED
GUILT	UNNOTICABLE				FLOODED
OTHER:	UNNOTICABLE				FLOODED

Today's date:

Additional feedback:

What I learned about myself today...

One thing I can do to care for myself tonight...

Today's date: _____   Days sober: _____

Day 5 Poison: **Stubbornness**

Ask the addictive mind:

- Why change?

- Is there anything wrong with what we're doing, or how we're behaving?

- Do we really want to change?

Mind's Story:

Feelings that arose

ANGER	1 *UNNOTICABLE*	2	3	4	5 *FLOODED*
FEAR	1 *UNNOTICABLE*	2	3	4	5 *FLOODED*
PAIN	1 *UNNOTICABLE*	2	3	4	5 *FLOODED*
JOY	1 *UNNOTICABLE*	2	3	4	5 *FLOODED*
PASSION	1 *UNNOTICABLE*	2	3	4	5 *FLOODED*
LOVE	1 *UNNOTICABLE*	2	3	4	5 *FLOODED*
SHAME	1 *UNNOTICABLE*	2	3	4	5 *FLOODED*
GUILT	1 *UNNOTICABLE*	2	3	4	5 *FLOODED*
OTHER:	1 *UNNOTICABLE*	2	3	4	5 *FLOODED*

Feedback received

Discrepancies between *Feelings that Arose* and *Feedback Received?*

"The secret of change is to focus

Day 5 Antidote: *Change*

Change brings chaos, and in chaos there is pain. There is no way around this simple equation: Change = Pain. Change is the only constant in life, and the only way out of pain is through change. It is a recipriocatly deterministic relationship; they mutually fuel each other. If we can't experience the pain, change will never happen.

By going through pain, you can find and experience *joy* and *relief*. We learn and become strong through the contrast of these emotions. We cannot have one without the other. For instance, there is no way to experience joy without the knowledge of sorrow. We don't know what safety is without experiencing fear. There is benefit to experiencing these contrasting emotions. Emotions are nothing more than the display of our own humanity. The changing in our emotions happens on a moment to moment basis, just like the changing of the winds. As winds can fill the sail, we as the captains of our own awareness can become skilled at casting our sails as best to navigate the turbulent waters. This can only be done through the acceptance of change.

Change is a natural process. Sometimes the pain can be overwhelming

all of your energy not on fighting the old, but on building the new."

—SOCRATES

and you may revert to the "comforts" of old habits. When the pain becomes this strong, embrace your own bravery and have faith that the joy and relief will come. It has to come: it is a natural law that one balances out the other. It will be naturally uncomfortable and chaotic, and that's okay. *You* are okay for experiencing these emotions. Remember that in contrast we learn, through learning we grow, and in growth there is change.

*E*xercise: To shed the delusions of the addictive mind one has to *look within*. **Sit in silence for 5 minutes.** Look within by asking yourself:

- What is one way I can invoke change today?

- How will change affect those around me?

৯৯

Notice how your body feels as you sit with these questions. For example, what are you feeling in your shoulders? In your arms? In your legs and feet? What emotions arise within? What thoughts come into your awareness? Give labels to your responses. "Shoulder tension," "sadness," "thinking," "anger," "frustration." Once labeled, bring your attention back to your breathing. Notice the rhythm of your breathing. If you find your attention drifting to other thoughts, label those thoughts briefly and bring your attention back to your breath.

When you have completed your meditation, reflect on what you became aware of and write them down on the next page. Include the emotions you felt. Share your reflection with the group and take note of their feedback. There is no right or wrong way to do this. You just simply need to do it.

Today's date: Days sober:

New Mind's Story:

Feelings that arose

ANGER	1 UNNOTICABLE	2	3	4	5 FLOODED
FEAR	1 UNNOTICABLE	2	3	4	5 FLOODED
PAIN	1 UNNOTICABLE	2	3	4	5 FLOODED
JOY	1 UNNOTICABLE	2	3	4	5 FLOODED
PASSION	1 UNNOTICABLE	2	3	4	5 FLOODED
LOVE	1 UNNOTICABLE	2	3	4	5 FLOODED
SHAME	1 UNNOTICABLE	2	3	4	5 FLOODED
GUILT	1 UNNOTICABLE	2	3	4	5 FLOODED
OTHER:	1 UNNOTICABLE	2	3	4	5 FLOODED

Today's date:

Additional feedback:

What I learned about myself today...

One thing I can do to care for myself tonight...

Today's date:

Additional feedback:

What I learned about myself today...

One thing I can do to care for myself tonight...

Today's date: Days sober:

Day 6 Poison: **Avoidance**

Ask the addictive mind:

- What aversions do we have today (tasks, treatment, work, family)?

- How does evading these tasks harm us?

- How does that make us elusive in our relationships?

*M*ind's *Story:*

Feelings that arose

	1	2	3	4	5
ANGER	UNNOTICABLE				FLOODED
FEAR	UNNOTICABLE				FLOODED
PAIN	UNNOTICABLE				FLOODED
JOY	UNNOTICABLE				FLOODED
PASSION	UNNOTICABLE				FLOODED
LOVE	UNNOTICABLE				FLOODED
SHAME	UNNOTICABLE				FLOODED
GUILT	UNNOTICABLE				FLOODED
OTHER:	UNNOTICABLE				FLOODED

Feedback received

Discrepancies between *Feelings that Arose* and *Feedback Received?*

Feedback received

Discrepancies between *Feelings that Arose* and *Feedback Received?*

"The price of greatness

Day 6 Antidote: *Responsibility*

The Ego often blames others for your lot in life. It is easy to get caught in this cycle.

> *I didn't get what I need, and it's all their fault. If they hadn't done that, I wouldn't be stuck in this mess! If they would only understand what I need, I wouldn't be doing my old behaviors! I can't do this because it's cold and raining. It's too hot and bright for me to do that.*

When you don't do what you need to do for yourself today, you end up blaming someone or something tomorrow. Be responsible for yourself *now*. Do not look for satisfaction and fulfillment from other people. A sense of entitlement that things should work out on their own in a manner satisfactory to you is false; nothing works out unless you create it—first in your mind, followed by body.

In addiction, addicts like to sit on the couch and whip themselves for all their past behaviors, and they believe this is taking responsibility, but it is not. Taking responsibility is standing up from the couch, admitting your faults, making amends for your mistakes by taking action to learn how not to do them again.

is responsibility. —WINSTON CHURCHILL

Your happiness, clarity, balance, peace, and enjoyment lie solely on yourself and what you do today. When you align with responsibilty today, you will reap integrity tomorrow. When you execute your healthy behaviors, especially when you don't want to, you will feel better about yourself and build esteem. When you stop blaming others, you will create an internal locus of control, leading to better choices and rewards.

*E*xercise: To shed the delusions of the addictive mind one has to *look within*. **Sit in silence for 5 minutes.** Look within by asking yourself:

- What is one thing I can take responsibility for?

- How can I start that responsibility today?

❧

Notice how your body feels as you sit with these questions. For example, what are you feeling in your shoulders? In your arms? In your legs and feet? What emotions arise within? What thoughts come into your awareness? Give labels to your responses. "Shoulder tension," "sadness," "thinking," "anger," "frustration." Once labeled, bring your attention back to your breathing. Notice the rhythm of your breathing. If you find your attention drifting to other thoughts, label those thoughts briefly and bring your attention back to your breath.

When you have completed your meditation, reflect on what you became aware of and write them down on the next page. Include the emotions you felt. Share your reflection with the group and take note of their feedback. There is no right or wrong way to do this. You just simply need to do it.

Day 6: Avoidance & Responsibility

Today's date: Days sober:

New Mind's Story:

Feelings that arose

	1	2	3	4	5
ANGER	UNNOTICABLE				FLOODED
FEAR	UNNOTICABLE				FLOODED
PAIN	UNNOTICABLE				FLOODED
JOY	UNNOTICABLE				FLOODED
PASSION	UNNOTICABLE				FLOODED
LOVE	UNNOTICABLE				FLOODED
SHAME	UNNOTICABLE				FLOODED
GUILT	UNNOTICABLE				FLOODED
OTHER:	UNNOTICABLE				FLOODED

Today's date:

Additional feedback:

What I learned about myself today...

One thing I can do to care for myself tonight...

Day 7: Hubris

Today's date: Days sober:

Day 7 Poison: **Hubris**

Ask the addictive mind:

- Does our addiction compare itself to others?

- Do we tell ourselves we're terminally unique?

- Do we tell ourselves our addiction is not as bad as others'?

Mind's Story:

Feelings that arose

ANGER	1 UNNOTICABLE	2	3	4	5 FLOODED
FEAR	1 UNNOTICABLE	2	3	4	5 FLOODED
PAIN	1 UNNOTICABLE	2	3	4	5 FLOODED
JOY	1 UNNOTICABLE	2	3	4	5 FLOODED
PASSION	1 UNNOTICABLE	2	3	4	5 FLOODED
LOVE	1 UNNOTICABLE	2	3	4	5 FLOODED
SHAME	1 UNNOTICABLE	2	3	4	5 FLOODED
GUILT	1 UNNOTICABLE	2	3	4	5 FLOODED
OTHER:	1 UNNOTICABLE	2	3	4	5 FLOODED

Feedback received

Discrepancies between *Feelings that Arose* and *Feedback Received?*

"With pride there are many

Day 7 Antidote: *Humility*

Our egos and addictive minds have full time jobs promoting our superiority. Finding faults in others and making our opinions heard are primary job objectives. (It is no wonder oblivion and ecstasy are their favorite places for vacation).

Our egos and addictive minds do not enjoy hearing about successes of others. The experiences of other people are constantly downplayed. Any achievements not their own are triggers for envy. Skirting honesty and harboring secrets are skills our egos and addictive minds have mastered. Shielding yourself with lies to keep our egos from deflating, omitting events that have happened and denying dark parts of our personalities are just some of these well-honed skills. This is Ego. This is what disconnects you from peace and balance.

There is strength in being humble. On first attempts, we spend a vast amount of determination and energy trying to be humble. To allow someone else to express their thoughts, share their experiences, and open their heart to you is practicing humility. It takes restraint to act only as a witness. It takes patience to be fully present without judgment. It takes

curses, with humilty there are many blessings." —EZRA TAFT BENSON

courage to lower your shield and be honest about your behaviors. When you are humble, you allow your true self to be known, which allows peace and balance into your life.

*E*xercise: To shed the delusions of the addictive mind one has to *look within.* **Sit in silence for 5 minutes.** Look within by asking yourself:

- How can I practice humility today?

- Is it worth it to lower my shield of lies for balance and peace?

&

Notice how your body feels as you sit with these questions. For example, what are you feeling in your shoulders? In your arms? In your legs and feet? What emotions arise within? What thoughts come into your awareness? Give labels to your responses. "Shoulder tension," "sadness," "thinking," "anger," "frustration." Once labeled, bring your attention back to your breathing. Notice the rhythm of your breathing. If you find your attention drifting to other thoughts, label those thoughts briefly and bring your attention back to your breath.

When you have completed your meditation, reflect on what you became aware of and write them down on the next page. Include the emotions you felt. Share your reflection with the group and take note of their feedback. There is no right or wrong way to do this. You just simply need to do it.

Today's date: Days sober:

New Mind's Story:

Feelings that arose

	1	2	3	4	5
ANGER	UNNOTICABLE				FLOODED
FEAR	UNNOTICABLE				FLOODED
PAIN	UNNOTICABLE				FLOODED
JOY	UNNOTICABLE				FLOODED
PASSION	UNNOTICABLE				FLOODED
LOVE	UNNOTICABLE				FLOODED
SHAME	UNNOTICABLE				FLOODED
GUILT	UNNOTICABLE				FLOODED
OTHER:	UNNOTICABLE				FLOODED

Today's date:

Additional feedback:

What I learned about myself today...

One thing I can do to care for myself tonight...

Today's date: Days sober:

Day 8 Poison: **Anger**

Ask the addictive mind:

- What are we so angry about?

- How do we know when we're angry?

- What has anger gotten us?

Mind's Story:

Feelings that arose

	1	2	3	4	5
ANGER	UNNOTICABLE				FLOODED
FEAR	UNNOTICABLE				FLOODED
PAIN	UNNOTICABLE				FLOODED
JOY	UNNOTICABLE				FLOODED
PASSION	UNNOTICABLE				FLOODED
LOVE	UNNOTICABLE				FLOODED
SHAME	UNNOTICABLE				FLOODED
GUILT	UNNOTICABLE				FLOODED
OTHER:	UNNOTICABLE				FLOODED

Feedback received

Discrepancies between *Feelings that Arose* and *Feedback Received?*

"Quiet the mind

Day 8 Antidote: *Forgiveness*

We cannot erase the past, but we can accept it as history. We can choose to live *today*, free from the failures of *yesterday*. To do so, one must forgive oneself. Forgiveness is not a feeling. Forgiveness is a commitment. You have to remember that anger is a natural emotion designed to solve problems. Its purpose is to protect what is healthy and valuable. Angry outbursts, however, do not solve problems; they only display a wounded part of your soul. There is much wisdom to be gained from anger. It can only be revealed by sitting with your distress non-reactively.

Forgiveness takes action. It's behaving in ways that allow you to be loved. Forgiveness is a practice of openly and honestly learning to be present with emotions (such as anger) that we find hard to tolerate with compassion and acceptance. Just as you are learning to practice forgiveness with yourself, so are your loved ones. There will be times when their anger is flooding, and their practice will be a struggle too. Learning to practice compassion with the ones we love is another way to strengthen forgiveness for ourselves.

Remember, despite the pain your addiction has caused, you are still

and the soul will speak."

—MA JAYA SATI BHAGAVATI

worthy of love and belonging. You have already demonstrated the ability to forgive yourself and love yourself if you are reading this.

*E*xercise: To shed the delusions of the addictive mind one has to *look within*. **Sit in silence for 5 minutes.** Look within by asking yourself:

- What freedom would practicing forgiveness bring?
- What would life look like if we invited forgiveness in?
- Do I give myself permission to be worthy of forgiveness?

❧

Notice how your body feels as you sit with these questions. For example, what are you feeling in your shoulders? In your arms? In your legs and feet? What emotions arise within? What thoughts come into your awareness? Give labels to your responses. "Shoulder tension," "sadness," "thinking," "anger," "frustration." Once labeled, bring your attention back to your breathing. Notice the rhythm of your breathing. If you find your attention drifting to other thoughts, label those thoughts briefly and bring your attention back to your breath.

When you have completed your meditation, reflect on what you became aware of and write them down on the next page. Include the emotions you felt. Share your reflection with the group and take note of their feedback. There is no right or wrong way to do this. You just simply need to do it.

Today's date: Days sober:

New Mind's Story:

Feelings that arose

ANGER	1 *UNNOTICABLE*	2	3	4	5 *FLOODED*
FEAR	1 *UNNOTICABLE*	2	3	4	5 *FLOODED*
PAIN	1 *UNNOTICABLE*	2	3	4	5 *FLOODED*
JOY	1 *UNNOTICABLE*	2	3	4	5 *FLOODED*
PASSION	1 *UNNOTICABLE*	2	3	4	5 *FLOODED*
LOVE	1 *UNNOTICABLE*	2	3	4	5 *FLOODED*
SHAME	1 *UNNOTICABLE*	2	3	4	5 *FLOODED*
GUILT	1 *UNNOTICABLE*	2	3	4	5 *FLOODED*
OTHER:	1 *UNNOTICABLE*	2	3	4	5 *FLOODED*

Today's date:

Additional feedback:

What I learned about myself today...

One thing I can do to care for myself tonight...

Today's date: Days sober:

Day 9 Poison: **Hate**

Ask the addictive mind:

- How has our hate allowed us to flourish?

- What can we do to make peace with our hatred?

Mind's Story:

Day 9: Hate

Feelings that arose

	1 UNNOTICABLE	2	3	4	5 FLOODED
ANGER	1	2	3	4	5
FEAR	1	2	3	4	5
PAIN	1	2	3	4	5
JOY	1	2	3	4	5
PASSION	1	2	3	4	5
LOVE	1	2	3	4	5
SHAME	1	2	3	4	5
GUILT	1	2	3	4	5
OTHER:	1	2	3	4	5

Feedback received

Discrepancies between *Feelings that Arose* and *Feedback Received?*

"In the moment when I truly

Day 9 Antidote: *Compassion*

It was a warm evening in Los Angeles when she heard the loud, firm knock at her door. She opened the door and was greeted by two detectives. *What has he gotten into now,* she wondered about her son. She was unprepared when they told her that her son had been shot and killed.

Grief-stricken, she attended the trial everyday, and towards the end was given the chance to address the killer himself. She looked directly into his eyes and with tears streaming down her cheeks, she stated very audibly in the courtroom, "I am going to kill you."

The 15-year old boy was given a three-year sentence, and she could not stop thinking about him. She was consumed with a never-ending hate, shock and grief that she had never known before. Six months later, she was bewildered to find herself visiting her son's killer.

Separated by glass, they sat face to face, awkwardness and a telephone connecting them. The boy informed her that in the past six months, no one had come to visit. In fact, he had no family at all. At the end of the visit, she deposited some money into his account for toiletries.

She began to visit him on a regular basis and when the boy was released at the age of 18, she asked him if he would like to stay with her for some time. Having no place to go, he reluctantly agreed. In the beginning, they barely spoke or saw each other, but as time passed,

understand my enemy, understand him enough to defeat him, then at that very moment, I also love him."

—ENDER'S GAME (ORSON CARD)

they began having regular conversations, and she began cooking him dinner. She got him a dog, and he was grateful. He found work and helped pay the utilities. Shortly before his 21st birthday, as they were eating dinner at the dining table, she asked him, "Do you remember what I said to you in the courtroom? That I was going to kill you?" The boy stopped chewing his food, frozen with fear. When he regained his composure, he answered, "Yes."

"Well, I did," she said. "The boy who was lost and filled with such hate as to kill my son no longer lives. Instead, you sit before me, a hard-working, loving young man who strives to be a gentle person. I want to ask you if I can adopt you as my son." The boy filled with tears and answered, "Yes."

It may be hard to believe, but this is a true story. A mother adopted the boy that killed her son. We are often hateful of our addiction. However, in order to kill it, we must first learn to love ourselves while understanding that we co-exist with our addiction. We must learn to give love to all of our selves, including our addiction. Our addiction is nothing more and nothing less than the inner child in us who is so deeply wounded.

*E*xercise: To shed the delusions of the addictive mind one has to *look within*. **Sit in silence for 5 minutes.** Look within by asking yourself:

- How can I love myself and co-exist with addiction?

- How can I be compassionate towards myself today?

- What wisdom has been gained from addiction?

🙢

Notice how your body feels as you sit with these questions. For example, what are you feeling in your shoulders? In your arms? In your legs and feet? What emotions arise within? What thoughts come into your awareness? Give labels to your responses. "Shoulder tension," "sadness," "thinking," "anger," "frustration." Once labeled, bring your attention back to your breathing. Notice the rhythm of your breathing. If you find your attention drifting to other thoughts, label those thoughts briefly and bring your attention back to your breath.

When you have completed your meditation, reflect on what you became aware of and write them down on the next page. Include the emotions you felt. Share your reflection with the group and take note of their feedback. There is no right or wrong way to do this. You just simply need to do it.

Today's date: Days sober:

New Mind's Story:

Feelings that arose

	UNNOTICABLE				FLOODED
ANGER	1	2	3	4	5
FEAR	1	2	3	4	5
PAIN	1	2	3	4	5
JOY	1	2	3	4	5
PASSION	1	2	3	4	5
LOVE	1	2	3	4	5
SHAME	1	2	3	4	5
GUILT	1	2	3	4	5
OTHER:	1	2	3	4	5

Day 9: Hate ✿ Compassion

Today's date:

Additional feedback:

What I learned about myself today...

One thing I can do to care for myself tonight...

Today's date: Days sober:

Day 10 Poison: **Secrecy**

Ask the addictive mind:

- What have we had to do to maintain secrecy?

- What does it feel like to hold secrets?

M*ind's Story:*

Feelings that arose

	1	2	3	4	5
ANGER	UNNOTICABLE				FLOODED
FEAR	UNNOTICABLE				FLOODED
PAIN	UNNOTICABLE				FLOODED
JOY	UNNOTICABLE				FLOODED
PASSION	UNNOTICABLE				FLOODED
LOVE	UNNOTICABLE				FLOODED
SHAME	UNNOTICABLE				FLOODED
GUILT	UNNOTICABLE				FLOODED
OTHER:	UNNOTICABLE				FLOODED

Feedback received

Discrepancies between *Feelings that Arose* and *Feedback Received?*

"Honesty is more than

Day 10 Antidote: *Honesty*

"We are only as sick as our secrets" is a line heard often in 12-step meetings and recovery programs, but what does this really mean? Is there hard science to support this claim, or is it just a clever quip to get people to open up?

It turns out that science does support the claim. In his book, *Opening Up by Writing it Down*, James W. Pennebaker describes the physiological changes that occur when a person discloses secrets and when a person is inhibited from doing so. One study, conducted by a clinical psychologist paired with an immunologist, had half of the participants write on superficial topics. The other half were asked to write about their deepest thoughts and feelings concerning a trauma they experienced. Both groups wrote for 20 minutes a day, four days a week. The latter group wrote on instances of rape, death, murder, child abuse, and other traumatic instances they witnessed or experienced directly. Understandably, they were upset at the end of each writing session.

Before the participants began writing, the researchers had drawn their blood. Their blood was drawn again after the last writing session

not lying. It is truth telling, truth speaking, truth living, and truth loving." —JJAMES E. FAUST

and six weeks later. From each of the blood samples, they extracted white blood cells and placed them in petri dishes containing mitogens. They found that compared to the group who wrote on trivial subjects, the trauma writing group displayed enhanced immune function. Their white blood cells had a significantly stronger response in the petri dishes with mitogens after the last writing session. This effect was still seen six weeks after. Their health care visits for illness also dropped compared to the non-trauma writing group.

Not only are anxiety and stress reported less frequently in those who reveal secrets, but the immune system strengthens, and T-cell counts increase. When we live in truth, there is no place for fear, and our bodies are healthier for it. When you live honestly, you find peace.

Glaser, R., & Kiecolt-Glaser, J.K. (1994). Handbook of Human Stress and Immunity. San Diego, CA: Academic Press.
Pennebaker, J.W. & Smyth, J.M. (2016). *Opening Up by Writing it Down, 3rd ed.* 19 - 21. New York, NY: The Guildford Press

*E*xercise: To shed the delusions of the addictive mind one has to *look within.* **Sit in silence for 5 minutes.** Look within by asking yourself:

- Who knows your whole story?

- How can I begin to live honestly?

&

Notice how your body feels as you sit with these questions. For example, what are you feeling in your shoulders? In your arms? In your legs and feet? What emotions arise within? What thoughts come into your awareness? Give labels to your responses. "Shoulder tension," "sadness," "thinking," "anger," "frustration." Once labeled, bring your attention back to your breathing. Notice the rhythm of your breathing. If you find your attention drifting to other thoughts, label those thoughts briefly and bring your attention back to your breath.

When you have completed your meditation, reflect on what you became aware of and write them down on the next page. Include the emotions you felt. Share your reflection with the group and take note of their feedback. There is no right or wrong way to do this. You just simply need to do it.

Today's date: Days sober:

New Mind's Story:

Feelings that arose

	1	2	3	4	5
ANGER	*UNNOTICABLE*	2	3	4	*FLOODED*
FEAR	*UNNOTICABLE*	2	3	4	*FLOODED*
PAIN	*UNNOTICABLE*	2	3	4	*FLOODED*
JOY	*UNNOTICABLE*	2	3	4	*FLOODED*
PASSION	*UNNOTICABLE*	2	3	4	*FLOODED*
LOVE	*UNNOTICABLE*	2	3	4	*FLOODED*
SHAME	*UNNOTICABLE*	2	3	4	*FLOODED*
GUILT	*UNNOTICABLE*	2	3	4	*FLOODED*
OTHER:	*UNNOTICABLE*	2	3	4	*FLOODED*

Today's date:

Additional feedback:

What I learned about myself today...

One thing I can do to care for myself tonight...

The First 10 Days Summary

Directions: Look for Worksheet A at the end of this book. Cut it out and return to this page. Review Feelings that Arose worksheets for the previous 10 days. You quantified your feelings twice per day--once after Ask the Addictive Mind and again after meditating. Add up the total number of points for each emotion from these worksheets. Shade in your result. The left side of each collumn should reflect the summation from Ask the Addictive Mind. The right side of the collumn reflects the summation after meditating.

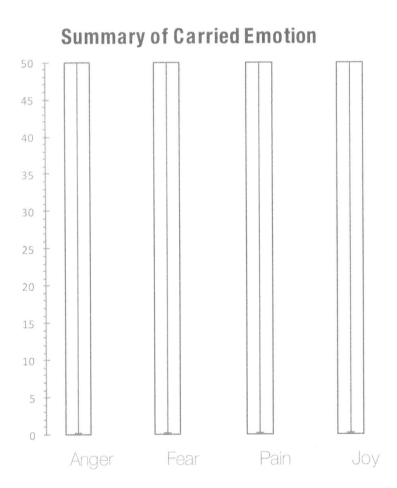

Summary of Carried Emotion

Summary of Carried Emotion

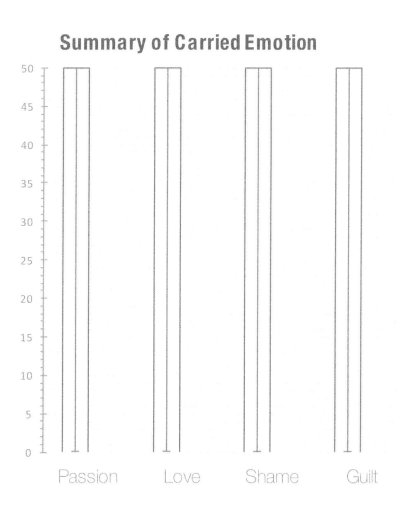

Days 11 - 20

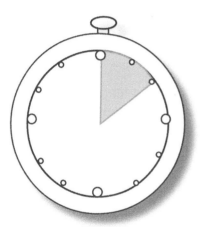

10 MINUTES
MEDITATION

Today's date: Days sober:

Day 11 Poison: **Greed**

Ask the addictive mind:

- When will enough be *enough?*

- How has greed helped you stay in power?

- What happens when you don't get what you want?

Mind's Story:

Feelings that arose

ANGER	1 UNNOTICABLE	2	3	4	5 FLOODED
FEAR	1 UNNOTICABLE	2	3	4	5 FLOODED
PAIN	1 UNNOTICABLE	2	3	4	5 FLOODED
JOY	1 UNNOTICABLE	2	3	4	5 FLOODED
PASSION	1 UNNOTICABLE	2	3	4	5 FLOODED
LOVE	1 UNNOTICABLE	2	3	4	5 FLOODED
SHAME	1 UNNOTICABLE	2	3	4	5 FLOODED
GUILT	1 UNNOTICABLE	2	3	4	5 FLOODED
OTHER:	1 UNNOTICABLE	2	3	4	5 FLOODED

Feedback received

Discrepancies between *Feelings that Arose* and *Feedback Received?*

"There is no exercise better

Day 11 Antidote: *Generosity*

Generosity is usually associated with monetary themes. We have all heard stories in which someone left a big tip for a waitress, or of a community coalescing to raise money for a neighbor in need. Generosity is broader than money.

Think about emotional generosity. How did you feel when you were last complimented for something you did? Are you generous with your compliments towards others? Have you ever been in a situation where a friend in need is calling, and you choose to decline the call? We have all been in situations like this, but this does not lead to emotional generosity. Think about a time when you needed somebody and you gained the courage to reach out for help only to be left without a response.

Part of recovery is about emotional generosity. The way that we get better is to be of service to others. There will always be someone who trailblazes the road for you and is there to help guide the way to recovery. It is now your duty, as part of the process of your own recovery, to maintain that trail for the next person's journey. To be a part of others' journey will not only reinforce your own learning in recovery but will also

for the heart than reaching down and lifting people up."

—JOHN HOLMES

create healthy relationships which shield you from the lure of addiction. Expand your definition of generosity and think about what you can do for others and yourself today. The more we give of ourselves in selfless ways, the more we distance ourselves from greed.

*E*xercise: To shed the delusions of the addictive mind one has to *look within*. **Sit in silence for 10 minutes.** Look within by asking yourself:

- What is one thing I can do today to be of service to myself?

- What is one thing I can do to be of service to others?

❧

Notice how your body feels as you sit with these questions. For example, what are you feeling in your shoulders? In your arms? In your legs and feet? What emotions arise within? What thoughts come into your awareness? Give labels to your responses. "Shoulder tension," "sadness," "thinking," "anger," "frustration." Once labeled, bring your attention back to your breathing. Notice the rhythm of your breathing. If you find your attention drifting to other thoughts, label those thoughts briefly and bring your attention back to your breath.

When you have completed your meditation, reflect on what you became aware of and write them down on the next page. Include the emotions you felt. Share your reflection with the group and take note of their feedback. There is no right or wrong way to do this. You just simply need to do it.

Today's date: Days sober:

New Mind's Story:

Feelings that arose

	1	2	3	4	5
ANGER	UNNOTICABLE				FLOODED
FEAR	UNNOTICABLE				FLOODED
PAIN	UNNOTICABLE				FLOODED
JOY	UNNOTICABLE				FLOODED
PASSION	UNNOTICABLE				FLOODED
LOVE	UNNOTICABLE				FLOODED
SHAME	UNNOTICABLE				FLOODED
GUILT	UNNOTICABLE				FLOODED
OTHER:	UNNOTICABLE				FLOODED

Today's date:

Additional feedback:

What I learned about myself today...

One thing I can do to care for myself tonight...

Today's date: Days sober:

Day 12 Poison: **Loathing**

Ask the addictive mind:

- How does loathing empower you to thrive?

- How does loathing keep us from healing?

Mind's Story:

Feelings that arose

ANGER	1 UNNOTICABLE	2	3	4	5 FLOODED
FEAR	1 UNNOTICABLE	2	3	4	5 FLOODED
PAIN	1 UNNOTICABLE	2	3	4	5 FLOODED
JOY	1 UNNOTICABLE	2	3	4	5 FLOODED
PASSION	1 UNNOTICABLE	2	3	4	5 FLOODED
LOVE	1 UNNOTICABLE	2	3	4	5 FLOODED
SHAME	1 UNNOTICABLE	2	3	4	5 FLOODED
GUILT	1 UNNOTICABLE	2	3	4	5 FLOODED
OTHER:	1 UNNOTICABLE	2	3	4	5 FLOODED

Feedback received

Discrepancies between *Feelings that Arose* and *Feedback Received?*

"Respect yourself, and

Day 12 Antidote: *Respect*

Our bodies are our temples. It is one thing when we are victims of abuse and have been physically mistreated. However, it is also one of the things that we have some control over. We get to decide how we treat our bodies.

Think about the way you treat yourself. Do you compulsively hurt your body by poor eating habits, self-defeating comments, bad hygiene, or unsafe sex practices? Today, think about what self-respect can look like.

Is a constant diet of drive-through food respectful to your body? No, of course not. Not everyone has their own time, or a loved one, to make a home-cooked dinner, but there are plenty of eating options healthier than fried take-out. When was the last time you practiced mindfully eating a nutritious meal? Taking care of our bodies involves making the effort and clearing time to sit down and enjoy fresh food, preferably without distraction or rushing so that you can actually enjoy what you taste.

What negative comments does the mind tell you about yourself that you may not be aware of? When looking in the mirror, does the mind tell you that you are fat, worthless, a loser, useless, a piece-of-shit? Do

others will respect you."

—CONFUCIUS

you ever tell yourself that you are no good? Do you hold the belief that you will never get ahead or get better in recovery? This is disrespect for yourself. This is where the addiction thrives.

Self-respect can take many forms: Paying your bills on time, making sure you get enough sleep, telling people, "no," or even brushing your teeth at night. From time to time, we faulter in treating ourselves with respect. Today, you have the power to turn that ship around.

When we tend to ourselves emotionally and physically, we begin to shed layers of our own personal neglect, and we start to value ourselves in ways that are new to us. Through self-respect, we begin to instill integrity and reestablish boundaries. We re-parent the wounded child within us, which will reflect in our dealings with others. Just as Confucius says, "Respect yourself and others will respect you."

*E*xercise: To shed the delusions of the addictive mind one has to *look within*. **Sit in silence for 10 minutes.** Look within by asking yourself:

- What is one self-respecting thing that you can do today?

- What is one respectful thing you can do for others?

&

Notice how your body feels as you sit with these questions. For example, what are you feeling in your shoulders? In your arms? In your legs and feet? What emotions arise within? What thoughts come into your awareness? Give labels to your responses. "Shoulder tension," "sadness," "thinking," "anger," "frustration." Once labeled, bring your attention back to your breathing. Notice the rhythm of your breathing. If you find your attention drifting to other thoughts, label those thoughts briefly and bring your attention back to your breath.

When you have completed your meditation, reflect on what you became aware of and write them down on the next page. Include the emotions you felt. Share your reflection with the group and take note of their feedback. There is no right or wrong way to do this. You just simply need to do it.

Today's date: Days sober:

New Mind's Story:

Feelings that arose

	1 UNNOTICABLE	2	3	4	5 FLOODED
ANGER	1 UNNOTICABLE	2	3	4	5 FLOODED
FEAR	1 UNNOTICABLE	2	3	4	5 FLOODED
PAIN	1 UNNOTICABLE	2	3	4	5 FLOODED
JOY	1 UNNOTICABLE	2	3	4	5 FLOODED
PASSION	1 UNNOTICABLE	2	3	4	5 FLOODED
LOVE	1 UNNOTICABLE	2	3	4	5 FLOODED
SHAME	1 UNNOTICABLE	2	3	4	5 FLOODED
GUILT	1 UNNOTICABLE	2	3	4	5 FLOODED
OTHER:	1 UNNOTICABLE	2	3	4	5 FLOODED

Today's date:

Additional feedback:

What I learned about myself today...

One thing I can do to care for myself tonight...

Today's date: Days sober:

Day 13 Poison: **Resistance**

Ask the addictive mind:

- What will happen if we continue resisting the recovery process?

- What is it like to be uncertain of the future?

Mind's Story:

Feelings that arose

	1	2	3	4	5
ANGER	UNNOTICABLE				FLOODED
FEAR	UNNOTICABLE				FLOODED
PAIN	UNNOTICABLE				FLOODED
JOY	UNNOTICABLE				FLOODED
PASSION	UNNOTICABLE				FLOODED
LOVE	UNNOTICABLE				FLOODED
SHAME	UNNOTICABLE				FLOODED
GUILT	UNNOTICABLE				FLOODED
OTHER:	UNNOTICABLE				FLOODED

Feedback received

Discrepancies between *Feelings that Arose* and *Feedback Received?*

"The mind is like a parachute.

Day 13 Antidote: *Open-Mindedness*

Needles, California is a small town along the banks of the Colorado River—a major tourist attraction on weekends and holidays. In that small town, you were either a local river rat or a weekender, and there was one thing the river rats knew that the weekenders didn't: How to stay alive in the water.

When weekenders swam, they would often get caught in the current, and their reaction was sadly predictable. They would panic and try to swim against the current back to their camp. Of course they would lose this battle. Rivers never tire whereas human beings do, especially with a full belly of food and drink. Needless to say, a drowning or two was expected on major holidays.

The river rats knew that if you got caught up in the current, the way to survive was to roll over on your back and flow with the river. As long as you didn't fight it, the river would always take care of you and bring you back to shore. It may not be the same shore you left from, and it may give you a long way to walk, but you would be alive to return to your loved ones.

It doesn't work unless you open it." —FRANK ZAPPA

Just like the river, life will continue to flow in the direction that is best for us. When we are caught in active addiction, we are attempting to swim against the current of life. Recovery is learning how to let go of what we *think* is best. It is doing what others who have been in recovery for some time *know* is best. To do this, we must live our lives in reflection. The way to openness is realizing that our thinking is flawed and has been problematic all along. We must be open to integrating the wisdom of others. Addiction uses the thoughts of the mind to convince us we must swim back to the beach from which we started, and this is a deadly cycle.

*E*xercise: To shed the delusions of the addictive mind one has to *look within*. **Sit in silence for 10 minutes.** Look within by asking yourself:

- What would it be like to surrender my ways of thinking?
- What would it be like to open up to the recovery process?

℘

Notice how your body feels as you sit with these questions. For example, what are you feeling in your shoulders? In your arms? In your legs and feet? What emotions arise within? What thoughts come into your awareness? Give labels to your responses. "Shoulder tension," "sadness," "thinking," "anger," "frustration." Once labeled, bring your attention back to your breathing. Notice the rhythm of your breathing. If you find your attention drifting to other thoughts, label those thoughts briefly and bring your attention back to your breath.

When you have completed your meditation, reflect on what you became aware of and write them down on the next page. Include the emotions you felt. Share your reflection with the group and take note of their feedback. There is no right or wrong way to do this. You just simply need to do it.

Today's date: Days sober:

New Mind's Story:

Feelings that arose

	1	2	3	4	5
ANGER	UNNOTICABLE				FLOODED
FEAR	UNNOTICABLE				FLOODED
PAIN	UNNOTICABLE				FLOODED
JOY	UNNOTICABLE				FLOODED
PASSION	UNNOTICABLE				FLOODED
LOVE	UNNOTICABLE				FLOODED
SHAME	UNNOTICABLE				FLOODED
GUILT	UNNOTICABLE				FLOODED
OTHER:	UNNOTICABLE				FLOODED

Today's date:

Additional feedback:

What I learned about myself today...

One thing I can do to care for myself tonight...

Day 14 Poison: **Enemies**

Ask the addictive mind:

- With whom do we feel safe sharing that we are in recovery?

- What could happen if we tell others we are in recovery?

- From whom do we hide our recovery?

Mind's Story:

Feelings that arose

ANGER	1 _UNNOTICABLE_	2	3	4	5 _FLOODED_
FEAR	1 _UNNOTICABLE_	2	3	4	5 _FLOODED_
PAIN	1 _UNNOTICABLE_	2	3	4	5 _FLOODED_
JOY	1 _UNNOTICABLE_	2	3	4	5 _FLOODED_
PASSION	1 _UNNOTICABLE_	2	3	4	5 _FLOODED_
LOVE	1 _UNNOTICABLE_	2	3	4	5 _FLOODED_
SHAME	1 _UNNOTICABLE_	2	3	4	5 _FLOODED_
GUILT	1 _UNNOTICABLE_	2	3	4	5 _FLOODED_
OTHER:	1 _UNNOTICABLE_	2	3	4	5 _FLOODED_

Feedback received

Discrepancies between *Feelings that Arose* and *Feedback Received?*

"If you cannot change the people

Day 14 Antidote: *Allies*

We live in a culture where we collect friends. The term *friend* has changed in meaning with the growth of social media. We can spend copious amounts of time adding and rearranging our friends, noting how many 'likes' our photos and posts generate. But do these 'likes' and 'friends' provide the support that we need? As we move forward in recovery, where are these friends? Have they been there for you in your time of need?

We need to have more than friends in our lives. We must have *allies*. Allies are people who know our whole story and who love us anyway (never purposefully using sensitive information to hurt us). They are people we can trust and count on. Think of the friends you have and the people you've 'friended.' Who among them can be called allies?

Anyone who gardens can tell you how nature has so many answers for us if we stop and listen for a moment. Life can be fruitful and abundant, but left unattended, things will overgrow. Weeds will sprout and mask the beauty of the garden, much like an expanded friend's list can make it difficult to see who is a true ally in your life. If you have a friend that continues to accept your self-defeating behaviors, you need to

around you, change the people you're around."

- ROY T. BENNETT

realize this is a counterfeit friendship. True friendships do not facilitate self-destructive behaviors.

A true ally would be there in our hour of need, encouraging us to reflect in a healthy way, telling us the truths about our flaws, even when they are hard to hear. A true ally would not continue to perpetuate chaos. As the old Irish proverb says, "Only real friends will tell you when your face is dirty."

*E*xercise: To shed the delusions of the addictive mind one has to *look within*. **Sit in silence for 10 minutes.** Look within by asking yourself:

- Which of my relationships encourage my growth in recovery?

- What allies do I have now?

&

Notice how your body feels as you sit with these questions. For example, what are you feeling in your shoulders? In your arms? In your legs and feet? What emotions arise within? What thoughts come into your awareness? Give labels to your responses. "Shoulder tension," "sadness," "thinking," "anger," "frustration." Once labeled, bring your attention back to your breathing. Notice the rhythm of your breathing. If you find your attention drifting to other thoughts, label those thoughts briefly and bring your attention back to your breath.

When you have completed your meditation, reflect on what you became aware of and write them down on the next page. Include the emotions you felt. Share your reflection with the group and take note of their feedback. There is no right or wrong way to do this. You just simply need to do it.

Today's date: Days sober:

New Mind's Story:

Feelings that arose

	1	2	3	4	5
ANGER	*UNNOTICABLE*				*FLOODED*
FEAR	*UNNOTICABLE*				*FLOODED*
PAIN	*UNNOTICABLE*				*FLOODED*
JOY	*UNNOTICABLE*				*FLOODED*
PASSION	*UNNOTICABLE*				*FLOODED*
LOVE	*UNNOTICABLE*				*FLOODED*
SHAME	*UNNOTICABLE*				*FLOODED*
GUILT	*UNNOTICABLE*				*FLOODED*
OTHER:	*UNNOTICABLE*				*FLOODED*

Today's date:

Additional feedback:

What I learned about myself today...

One thing I can do to care for myself tonight...

Today's date: Days sober:

Day 15 Poison: **Self-Absorption**

Ask the addictive mind:

- When have you done a "selfless act" in
  order to gain something from somebody else?

Mind's Story:

Feelings that arose

	1	2	3	4	5
ANGER	UNNOTICABLE				FLOODED
FEAR	1 UNNOTICABLE	2	3	4	5 FLOODED
PAIN	1 UNNOTICABLE	2	3	4	5 FLOODED
JOY	1 UNNOTICABLE	2	3	4	5 FLOODED
PASSION	1 UNNOTICABLE	2	3	4	5 FLOODED
LOVE	1 UNNOTICABLE	2	3	4	5 FLOODED
SHAME	1 UNNOTICABLE	2	3	4	5 FLOODED
GUILT	1 UNNOTICABLE	2	3	4	5 FLOODED
OTHER:	1 UNNOTICABLE	2	3	4	5 FLOODED

Feedback received

Discrepancies between *Feelings that Arose* and *Feedback Received?*

"Ego is the only requirement

Day 15 Antidote: *Oblivion of Ego*

The Buddhist monk was filled with fear and worry as he began his period of meditation, alone in a cave in the Himalayas. Even with his experience, the adjustment to this new environment was difficult and longer than he had anticipated. After a month, he managed to carve out a well-disciplined schedule for himself. In the mornings he would meditate until the sunlight reached the opening of his cave. He would then scavenge the mountain-side for wood and food. Upon return he would meditate until the sunlight dictated that he start a fire for the night's warmth. It was a difficult way to live, but he was not seeking pleasure.

One afternoon with logs and food in his arms, he returned to his cave to find it was being used. After the initial shock of disbelief, he became flushed with anger so quickly he forgot his monk-ness and yelled, "What are you doing here? Get out of my cave!" He did not see who was inside, but he heard their laughter. This made the monk more upset, but the quickly vanishing sunlight grounded him enough to drop the logs outside his occupied cave and start the fire, lest he freeze to death. Once lit, he threw rocks inside his cave to drive the occupants out. The more rocks he threw, the harder they laughed. When he realized this was futile, he sat by the fire to meditate. It was warmer there, and the unexpected confrontation had drained him.

He could hear the occupants talking amongst themselves as he meditated

to destroy any relationship."

—EVAN CARMICHAEL

but he kept still, continually coming back to his breath, even when he heard them stepping out of his cave. He felt the poke of a stick on his shoulder and a swat on his back. He felt the ground move and heard the thuds as one of the occupants joyously jumped up and over him repeatedly, singing all the while. After more mockery and shenanigans, the monk finally opened his eyes and spoke, this time calmly: "I want you three to know that I will no longer fight you, nor will I try to ignore you." He got up from the fire and offered the occupants the mushrooms and fruit he gathered earlier. The occupants apparently had no appetite and left the monk to be.

§ə

This story is known as *"The Monk and the Three Demons."* Of course, the demons were constructs of the monk's own mind. Our minds, specifically our *ego*, will construct stories which simply are not based in reality. They are fantasies created to gain a sense of certainty. In our addiction we have always given into the addictive mind's stories. We became self-absorbed and spun a tale of how we have to act out *now*, how this will be the *last time*, how if we don't do something, the distress we feel will *never go away*. These stories are usually powerful enough to pull us out of recovery, but if there is any resistance left, the addictive mind has one last trick up it's sleeve: It convinces us that *we must always be right.*

*E*xercise: To shed the delusions of the addictive mind one has to *look within*. **Sit in silence for 10 minutes.** Look within by asking yourself:

- What would it be like to accept uncertainty in life?

- What would happen if you allowed yourself to sit in discomfort and not attempt to extinguish it?

- What demons will I befriend by sitting with my discomfort?

❧

Notice how your body feels as you sit with these questions. For example, what are you feeling in your shoulders? In your arms? In your legs and feet? What emotions arise within? What thoughts come into your awareness? Give labels to your responses. "Shoulder tension," "sadness," "thinking," "anger," "frustration." Once labeled, bring your attention back to your breathing. Notice the rhythm of your breathing. If you find your attention drifting to other thoughts, label those thoughts briefly and bring your attention back to your breath.

When you have completed your meditation, reflect on what you became aware of and write them down on the next page. Include the emotions you felt. Share your reflection with the group and take note of their feedback. There is no right or wrong way to do this. You just simply need to do it.

Today's date: Days sober:

New Mind's Story:

Feelings that arose

	1 UNNOTICABLE	2	3	4	5 FLOODED
ANGER	1 UNNOTICABLE	2	3	4	5 FLOODED
FEAR	1 UNNOTICABLE	2	3	4	5 FLOODED
PAIN	1 UNNOTICABLE	2	3	4	5 FLOODED
JOY	1 UNNOTICABLE	2	3	4	5 FLOODED
PASSION	1 UNNOTICABLE	2	3	4	5 FLOODED
LOVE	1 UNNOTICABLE	2	3	4	5 FLOODED
SHAME	1 UNNOTICABLE	2	3	4	5 FLOODED
GUILT	1 UNNOTICABLE	2	3	4	5 FLOODED
OTHER:	1 UNNOTICABLE	2	3	4	5 FLOODED

Today's date:

Additional feedback:

What I learned about myself today...

One thing I can do to care for myself tonight...

Today's date: Days sober:

Day 16 Poison: **Disregard**

Ask the addictive mind:

- What parts of our life do we disregard when we act out?

- What help do we disregard?

- How does disregarding elicit chaos?

Mind's Story:

Feelings that arose

ANGER	1 UNNOTICABLE	2	3	4	5 FLOODED
FEAR	1 UNNOTICABLE	2	3	4	5 FLOODED
PAIN	1 UNNOTICABLE	2	3	4	5 FLOODED
JOY	1 UNNOTICABLE	2	3	4	5 FLOODED
PASSION	1 UNNOTICABLE	2	3	4	5 FLOODED
LOVE	1 UNNOTICABLE	2	3	4	5 FLOODED
SHAME	1 UNNOTICABLE	2	3	4	5 FLOODED
GUILT	1 UNNOTICABLE	2	3	4	5 FLOODED
OTHER:	1 UNNOTICABLE	2	3	4	5 FLOODED

Feedback received

Discrepancies between *Feelings that Arose* and *Feedback Received?*

"What we pay attention to

Day 16 Antidote: *Attention*

Before the advent of iPads, kids had to make their own games to keep themselves entertained on a long family road trip. "Slugbug" is one such invention played by scanning the road behind and the road ahead for Volkswagen Beetles. The sibling or friend who saw one first would hit the other kid on the shoulder as hard as they could and yell out, "Slugbug!"

It's not hard to imagine the pain of getting slugged and the anticipation of slugging to keep kids occupied cross-country. Perhaps you've played this game yourself. It's easy to miss a Volkswagen Beetle coming at you from behind or even coming towards you on a busy highway, but over time, the ability to see specific cars increases. Shapes on the horizon that were once indistinguishable are easily categorized, or at least discounted as not being Volkswagen Beetles.

Whatever we focus on, our brains will make and wire the neurons to keep our attention on it, whether that be a specific car on the road, a drug of choice, or things of a sexual nature. Our ability to notice more of the object of our desire grows as we place attention on it.

Here's the good news: A mind trained over the years to focus on

expands.   What we pay
attention to we become." —BRENDA SHOSHANNA

something (whether consciously or not) will need time to be retrained, but it is possible. The plasticity of our minds allows it to be. Recovery is about reallocating your mind to healthy things and developing new neuronal connections in the process. What we attune to becomes our life.

*E*xercise: To shed the delusions of the addictive mind one has to *look within*. **Sit in silence for 10 minutes.** Look within by asking yourself:

- With whom will I choose to place my attention?

- On what will I choose to place my attention?

&a

Notice how your body feels as you sit with these questions. For example, what are you feeling in your shoulders? In your arms? In your legs and feet? What emotions arise within? What thoughts come into your awareness? Give labels to your responses. "Shoulder tension," "sadness," "thinking," "anger," "frustration." Once labeled, bring your attention back to your breathing. Notice the rhythm of your breathing. If you find your attention drifting to other thoughts, label those thoughts briefly and bring your attention back to your breath.

When you have completed your meditation, reflect on what you became aware of and write them down on the next page. Include the emotions you felt. Share your reflection with the group and take note of their feedback. There is no right or wrong way to do this. You just simply need to do it.

Today's date: Days sober:

*N*ew Mind's Story:

Feelings that arose

	1	2	3	4	5
ANGER	*UNNOTICABLE*				*FLOODED*
FEAR	*UNNOTICABLE*				*FLOODED*
PAIN	*UNNOTICABLE*				*FLOODED*
JOY	*UNNOTICABLE*				*FLOODED*
PASSION	*UNNOTICABLE*				*FLOODED*
LOVE	*UNNOTICABLE*				*FLOODED*
SHAME	*UNNOTICABLE*				*FLOODED*
GUILT	*UNNOTICABLE*				*FLOODED*
OTHER:	*UNNOTICABLE*				*FLOODED*

Today's date:

Additional feedback:

What I learned about myself today...

One thing I can do to care for myself tonight...

Today's date: Days sober:

Day 17 Poison: **Addiction**

Ask the addictive mind:

- How have you helped me survive?

- Remind me of the times you have protected me.

- What would it look like if we worked together?

Mind's Story:

Feelings that arose

	1	2	3	4	5
ANGER	UNNOTICABLE				FLOODED
FEAR	UNNOTICABLE				FLOODED
PAIN	UNNOTICABLE				FLOODED
JOY	UNNOTICABLE				FLOODED
PASSION	UNNOTICABLE				FLOODED
LOVE	UNNOTICABLE				FLOODED
SHAME	UNNOTICABLE				FLOODED
GUILT	UNNOTICABLE				FLOODED
OTHER:	UNNOTICABLE				FLOODED

Feedback received

Discrepancies between *Feelings that Arose* and *Feedback Received?*

"It's not survival of the fittest

Day 17 Antidote: *Nurturing*

In our active addiction the mind nurtures the art of distraction. It engages in a restless permute of different ways to distract our awareness of emotion. So, days becomes weeks, weeks become years, & years become decades. During this time our abilities to understand what emotions feel like, and to tolerate the emotional energy that arises within, atrophies.

As this continues we fall further into the abyss. Soon, the slightest event that stimulates an emotional charge becomes overwhelming, and we react with an impulsive behavior. It can be yelling, it can be avoiding, it can be clinging on to something. We become obsessed with whatever we can do to avoid feeling the emotion.

This is H.O.W.

- Honesty,

- Open-mind, open-heart

- Willingness to follow suggestion

as Darwin said; it's survival of the nurtured." —TARA BRACH

In recovery, we choose to nurture our ability to feel. This can only come from *honesty*. We must be honest to those who are in our recovery community. We must be *open* to accept feedback and have *willingness* to follow the suggestions of those who are farther along the path of recovery than we are.

We heal and begin to nurture our ability to accept life as it is instead of how we wish it was. We must do this no matter what. The natural reaction of the addictive mind is to vigorously reject those healthy alternatives being suggested. You must listen to them and follow through on their suggestions regardless of how much your mind tells you that those in recovery are mistaken. It is the past conditioning of your mind that brought you to nurture your addiction.

You can no longer trust those old perceptions even though every part of your mind is screaming not to. You must now step out from the abyss into the unknown, believing you will be loved, trusting those around you.

*E*xercise: To shed the delusions of the addictive mind one has to *look within*. **Sit in silence for 10 minutes.** Look within by asking yourself:

- How is it freeing to notice healthy ways to care for myself?

- What opportunities do I have to focus attention on healthy behaviors?

- What do I visualize my life to be like after five years of recovery?

❧

Notice how your body feels as you sit with these questions. For example, what are you feeling in your shoulders? In your arms? In your legs and feet? What emotions arise within? What thoughts come into your awareness? Give labels to your responses. "Shoulder tension," "sadness," "thinking," "anger," "frustration." Once labeled, bring your attention back to your breathing. Notice the rhythm of your breathing. If you find your attention drifting to other thoughts, label those thoughts briefly and bring your attention back to your breath.

When you have completed your meditation, reflect on what you became aware of and write them down on the next page. Include the emotions you felt. Share your reflection with the group and take note of their feedback. There is no right or wrong way to do this. You just simply need to do it.

Today's date: Days sober:

New Mind's Story:

Feelings that arose

	1	2	3	4	5
ANGER	UNNOTICABLE				FLOODED
FEAR	UNNOTICABLE				FLOODED
PAIN	UNNOTICABLE				FLOODED
JOY	UNNOTICABLE				FLOODED
PASSION	UNNOTICABLE				FLOODED
LOVE	UNNOTICABLE				FLOODED
SHAME	UNNOTICABLE				FLOODED
GUILT	UNNOTICABLE				FLOODED
OTHER:	UNNOTICABLE				FLOODED

Today's date:

Additional feedback:

What I learned about myself today...

One thing I can do to care for myself tonight...

Today's date: _____   Days sober: _____

Day 18 Poison: **Seduction**

Ask the addictive mind:

- In what ways have you motivated me to take advantage of others?

- What times have you driven me to abandon others and/or myself?

Mind's Story:

Feelings that arose

ANGER	1 UNNOTICABLE	2	3	4	5 FLOODED
FEAR	1 UNNOTICABLE	2	3	4	5 FLOODED
PAIN	1 UNNOTICABLE	2	3	4	5 FLOODED
JOY	1 UNNOTICABLE	2	3	4	5 FLOODED
PASSION	1 UNNOTICABLE	2	3	4	5 FLOODED
LOVE	1 UNNOTICABLE	2	3	4	5 FLOODED
SHAME	1 UNNOTICABLE	2	3	4	5 FLOODED
GUILT	1 UNNOTICABLE	2	3	4	5 FLOODED
OTHER:	1 UNNOTICABLE	2	3	4	5 FLOODED

Feedback received

Discrepancies between *Feelings that Arose* and *Feedback Received?*

"Daring to set boundaries

Day 18 Antidote: *Boundaries*

As we create a new life story, the single most important thing you can do for yourself is to set boundaries. We all have an internal compass—a feeling inside that tells us what is okay and what is *not* okay. This internal compass governs our boundaries. They are the *yes's* and the *no's* to the choices we face. They are the key to self-love and the way to love others.

There are two types of boundaries. A *protection boundary* is just that—a limit set to protect yourself from feeling hurt. A *containment boundary* is one that keeps you from spilling out onto others. Both types help define and enforce your value system, protecting you from lessening your integrity and self-respect to please another. Pleasing others at the expense of our values is something we all do from time to time to avoid discomfort, and that makes setting boundaries difficult. We like to please people, but what is the cost?

Boundaries are likely to unleash emotions within you and/or others. For example, you may have to set boundaries when you determine someone is not a safe person to be with. Saying *no* to this person may leave you with strong feelings of disappointment and disstress. The person you

is about having the courage to love ourselves even when we risk disappointing others."

— BRENÉ BROWN

said *no* to may become angry, and that may intensify your distress, but you have to remember that the discomfort is temporary. On the other hand, saying *yes* to this person may avoid uncomfortable feelings at that time, but it can leave you operating with a broken compass and take you down an unintended negative path. Boundaries are not walls; they are there to cultivate respect and take care of you.

*E*xercise: To shed the delusions of the addictive mind one has to *look within*. **Sit in silence for 10 minutes.** Look within by asking yourself:

- When have you set a firm boundary and were glad you did?

- When have you not trusted your compass but wished you had?

- What boundaries do you feel you should set up today?

&

Notice how your body feels as you sit with these questions. For example, what are you feeling in your shoulders? In your arms? In your legs and feet? What emotions arise within? What thoughts come into your awareness? Give labels to your responses. "Shoulder tension," "sadness," "thinking," "anger," "frustration." Once labeled, bring your attention back to your breathing. Notice the rhythm of your breathing. If you find your attention drifting to other thoughts, label those thoughts briefly and bring your attention back to your breath.

When you have completed your meditation, reflect on what you became aware of and write them down on the next page. Include the emotions you felt. Share your reflection with the group and take note of their feedback. There is no right or wrong way to do this. You just simply need to do it.

Today's date: Days sober:

New Mind's Story:

Feelings that arose

	1	2	3	4	5
ANGER	*UNNOTICABLE*				*FLOODED*
FEAR	*UNNOTICABLE*				*FLOODED*
PAIN	*UNNOTICABLE*				*FLOODED*
JOY	*UNNOTICABLE*				*FLOODED*
PASSION	*UNNOTICABLE*				*FLOODED*
LOVE	*UNNOTICABLE*				*FLOODED*
SHAME	*UNNOTICABLE*				*FLOODED*
GUILT	*UNNOTICABLE*				*FLOODED*
OTHER:	*UNNOTICABLE*				*FLOODED*

Today's date:

Additional feedback:

What I learned about myself today...

One thing I can do to care for myself tonight...

Today's date: Days sober:

Day 19 Poison: **Relapse**

Ask the addictive mind:

- What stories have you created to keep us locked up in fear and reclusion?

- What is the cost of relapse for us?

- How can we work together after a relapse?

Mind's Story:

Feelings that arose

	1	2	3	4	5
ANGER	UNNOTICABLE				FLOODED
FEAR	UNNOTICABLE				FLOODED
PAIN	UNNOTICABLE				FLOODED
JOY	UNNOTICABLE				FLOODED
PASSION	UNNOTICABLE				FLOODED
LOVE	UNNOTICABLE				FLOODED
SHAME	UNNOTICABLE				FLOODED
GUILT	UNNOTICABLE				FLOODED
OTHER:	UNNOTICABLE				FLOODED

Feedback received

Discrepancies between *Feelings that Arose* and *Feedback Received?*

"Awareness is like the sun.

Day 19 Antidote: *Awareness*

Imagine one morning you wake up to find you've been locked up in a prison cell. You are shocked. You have no idea how you got here. You shake the cell gate, but you realize the bars are not locked and the gate is slightly ajar. You are too terrified to open the gate further. You wonder if this is a test—that if you open the gate, the guards might appear and beat you down for trying to escape. So, you return to your bench and sit.

Time passes, no one comes by your cell, no one else seems to be in the building, and you are getting hungry. Your discomfort grows, but you try to cope and be patient. Finally, you decide something's not right, and out of anger and hunger you get up from your bench and head out for the gate. You push the gate and it squeaks loudly. You are sure the guards will respond to the noise. So instead of walking out, you go back to your bench and sit.

Time goes by and no one comes. You manage the courage to step out of your cell, into the hallway, looking both ways for signs of harm coming your way. The prison is dark. It's hard to see. You ignore your breath and listen for any sounds within the prison. You walk down the

when it shines on things, they are transformed."

—THICH NHAT HANH

concrete hallway and come to a metal door. You are sure that once you open and walk through the door, someone will be waiting for you, and it won't be a pleasant encounter. After hesitating, you turn the door handle and push it forward.

You stumble into sunlight, and it blinds you. Coming from a dim, damp corridor, the heat burns your skin, you fall to the ground. You get up to go back inside. As you rise, your eyes adjust and you take in the vibrant scenery. The sun ceases to burn your skin, and its warmth is actually comforting you in a surprising way. As you look around, the people you avoided are no longer frightening. Some of them you even love, and you are filled with the intuition that the feeling is mutual.

It is only then that you gain the *wisdom* to see the prison you were in was self-fabricated, that you were your own jail keeper. You were the guard, you had the keys to leave your cell the whole time. As we proceed through recovery, we begin to realize that we are not our *mind's stories*. We are merely the observer of our feelings, thoughts, and beliefs.

Awareness is understanding that we have choices. You don't gain awareness without stepping out into the unknown and embracing those frightening choices.

*E*xercise: To shed the delusions of the addictive mind one has to *look within*. **Sit in silence for 10 minutes.** Look within by asking yourself:

- How is life going to change with awareness?

- Am I ready for the new freedom that comes with recovery?

❧

Notice how your body feels as you sit with these questions. For example, what are you feeling in your shoulders? In your arms? In your legs and feet? What emotions arise within? What thoughts come into your awareness? Give labels to your responses. "Shoulder tension," "sadness," "thinking," "anger," "frustration." Once labeled, bring your attention back to your breathing. Notice the rhythm of your breathing. If you find your attention drifting to other thoughts, label those thoughts briefly and bring your attention back to your breath.

When you have completed your meditation, reflect on what you became aware of and write them down on the next page. Include the emotions you felt. Share your reflection with the group and take note of their feedback. There is no right or wrong way to do this. You just simply need to do it.

Today's date: Days sober:

New Mind's Story:

Feelings that arose

	1 UNNOTICABLE	2	3	4	5 FLOODED
ANGER	1 UNNOTICABLE	2	3	4	5 FLOODED
FEAR	1 UNNOTICABLE	2	3	4	5 FLOODED
PAIN	1 UNNOTICABLE	2	3	4	5 FLOODED
JOY	1 UNNOTICABLE	2	3	4	5 FLOODED
PASSION	1 UNNOTICABLE	2	3	4	5 FLOODED
LOVE	1 UNNOTICABLE	2	3	4	5 FLOODED
SHAME	1 UNNOTICABLE	2	3	4	5 FLOODED
GUILT	1 UNNOTICABLE	2	3	4	5 FLOODED
OTHER:	1 UNNOTICABLE	2	3	4	5 FLOODED

Today's date:

Additional feedback:

What I learned about myself today...

One thing I can do to care for myself tonight...

Today's date: Days sober:

Day 20 Poison: Resentment

Ask the addictive mind:

- What grievences do you still hold onto?

Mind's Story:

Feelings that arose

ANGER	1 UNNOTICABLE	2	3	4	5 FLOODED
FEAR	1 UNNOTICABLE	2	3	4	5 FLOODED
PAIN	1 UNNOTICABLE	2	3	4	5 FLOODED
JOY	1 UNNOTICABLE	2	3	4	5 FLOODED
PASSION	1 UNNOTICABLE	2	3	4	5 FLOODED
LOVE	1 UNNOTICABLE	2	3	4	5 FLOODED
SHAME	1 UNNOTICABLE	2	3	4	5 FLOODED
GUILT	1 UNNOTICABLE	2	3	4	5 FLOODED
OTHER:	1 UNNOTICABLE	2	3	4	5 FLOODED

Feedback received

Discrepancies between *Feelings that Arose* and *Feedback Received?*

"Change is never easy.

Day 20 Antidote: *Letting Go*

Two monks were traveling together. At one point, they came to a river with a strong current. As the monks were preparing to cross the river, they saw a woman also attempting to cross with much difficulty. The young woman asked if they could help her cross to the other side.

Both monks were silent for a time. One of the vows that monks live by is to have no physical contact with women.

Then, without a word, one of the monks picked up the woman, carried her across the river to the other side and continued on his journey with his companion in silence.

The other monk couldn't believe what had just happened. For the rest of the journey he was plagued by negative thoughts. He was angry that his companion dishonored their vows and couldn't make any sense of it. When they arrived at their destination, the other monk could not contain his fury any longer and blurted out, "As a monk, how could you touch that woman when we are not permitted to touch any woman? You have betrayed your vows."

The first monk looked at him and replied softly, "I helped a woman

You fight to hold on and you fight to let go." —UNKNOWN

cross the river and set her down days ago. I should be asking you, why are *you* still carrying her around?"

৪৯

This is a Zen story about how often we carry around resentments when they are lost on others. We have all experienced times in our lives when other people say things or do things that are painful. We can choose to ruminate over past actions or events, but it will ultimately amount to nothing. Instead, we can choose to let go of past anger. Letting go does not mean getting over it. Letting go is a mindful choice to no longer allow another's actions or words to have power over us. Letting go is a choice to surrender and accept what is.

*E*xercise: To shed the delusions of the addictive mind one has to *look within*. **Sit in silence for 10 minutes.** Look within by asking yourself:

- What would it be like to let go of my (our) resentments?

- What is keeping me from letting them go?

- What would be the first step to letting go?

✑

Notice how your body feels as you sit with these questions. For example, what are you feeling in your shoulders? In your arms? In your legs and feet? What emotions arise within? What thoughts come into your awareness? Give labels to your responses. "Shoulder tension," "sadness," "thinking," "anger," "frustration." Once labeled, bring your attention back to your breathing. Notice the rhythm of your breathing. If you find your attention drifting to other thoughts, label those thoughts briefly and bring your attention back to your breath.

When you have completed your meditation, reflect on what you became aware of and write them down on the next page. Include the emotions you felt. Share your reflection with the group and take note of their feedback. There is no right or wrong way to do this. You just simply need to do it.

Today's date: Days sober:

New Mind's Story:

Feelings that arose

ANGER	1 UNNOTICABLE	2	3	4	5 FLOODED
FEAR	1 UNNOTICABLE	2	3	4	5 FLOODED
PAIN	1 UNNOTICABLE	2	3	4	5 FLOODED
JOY	1 UNNOTICABLE	2	3	4	5 FLOODED
PASSION	1 UNNOTICABLE	2	3	4	5 FLOODED
LOVE	1 UNNOTICABLE	2	3	4	5 FLOODED
SHAME	1 UNNOTICABLE	2	3	4	5 FLOODED
GUILT	1 UNNOTICABLE	2	3	4	5 FLOODED
OTHER:	1 UNNOTICABLE	2	3	4	5 FLOODED

Today's date:

Additional feedback:

What I learned about myself today...

One thing I can do to care for myself tonight...

Days 11 - 20 Summary

Directions: Look for Worksheet B at the end of this book. Cut it out and return to this page. Review Feelings that Arose worksheets for the previous 10 days. You quantified your feelings twice per day--once after Ask the Addictive Mind and again after meditating. Add up the total number of points for each emotion from these worksheets. Shade in your result. The left side of each collumn should reflect the summation from Ask the Addictive Mind. The right side of the collumn reflects the summation after meditating.

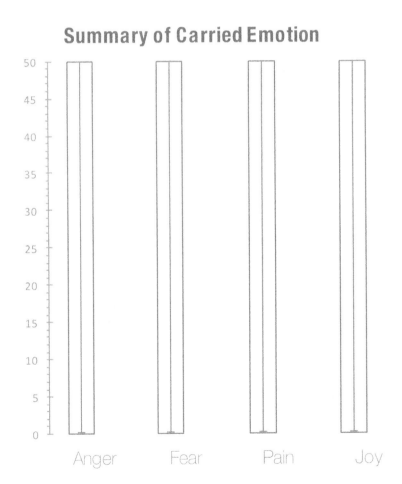

Days 11 - 20

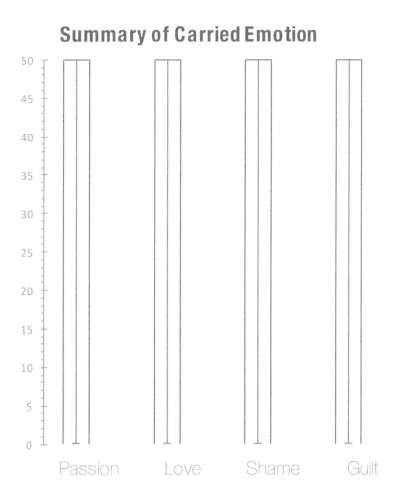

Summary of Carried Emotion

Days 21 - 30

15 MINUTES
MEDITATION

Today's date: Days sober:

Day 21 Poison: **Pride**

Ask the addictive mind:

- What are the signs that we are being prideful?

- What is our image trying to convey?

Mind's Story:

Feelings that arose

ANGER	1 UNNOTICABLE	2	3	4	5 FLOODED
FEAR	1 UNNOTICABLE	2	3	4	5 FLOODED
PAIN	1 UNNOTICABLE	2	3	4	5 FLOODED
JOY	1 UNNOTICABLE	2	3	4	5 FLOODED
PASSION	1 UNNOTICABLE	2	3	4	5 FLOODED
LOVE	1 UNNOTICABLE	2	3	4	5 FLOODED
SHAME	1 UNNOTICABLE	2	3	4	5 FLOODED
GUILT	1 UNNOTICABLE	2	3	4	5 FLOODED
OTHER:	1 UNNOTICABLE	2	3	4	5 FLOODED

Feedback received

Discrepancies between *Feelings that Arose* and *Feedback Received?*

"To be yourself in a world

Day 21 Antidote: *Accomplishment*

It was an ideal Spring morning with sunshine, a light breeze, and no humidity. Looking out of the window, he longed to step out. He was scared, lost, overwhelmed, and physically weak. She came into the room and asked politely, "How are you doing? I am your physical therapist. Today we are going to start to teach you how to walk again."

She moved his bed upwards to sit him up. She asked permission to remove the oxygen tubes from his nose. He agreed, but regretted it immediately. He began to feel tingling in his hands and began to gasp. She was startled and asked, "What's wrong?" but he could not reply as he struggled with each breath. His skin turned pale, then blue, and he grabbed the tubes and put them back into his nose.

"Okay," she said, "we will teach you to walk again with oxygen." She smiled and warned him it was his first day, so they would begin by getting out of bed and into the chair against the nearby wall. He was excited for the challenge of getting off the bed where he had been bound the past two weeks. He sat up and began to swing his legs over the side of the bed. He felt lightheaded, but he was eager to try standing. He took a few deep breaths then stood on his feet. He felt surprised at how heavy the body felt. He was determined to make it to the chair.

The physical therapist aided his slow, wobble walk and they reached

that is constantly trying to make you someone else is the greatest accomplishment." –RALPH WALDO EMERSON

his goal together. He sat down on the chair and thought, *What a relief to sit!* He felt like he had run miles. After a time, they made it back to his bed. She encouraged him that each day he would improve by small but significant increments.

As days went by, they would meet for their walking exercises, and each time they would walk a little farther. One day to the door, the next day into the hallway, and after a time, he was able to walk to the lunchroom without oxygen support. The day he was discharged, he was determined to walk out on his own, and he did so carrying his own bag. He can still remember the way the sun felt as he stepped out of the hospital doors, as if he was feeling the warmth for the first time.

As we proceed on our path of recovery there is much we are grateful for. Our hard work allows us to improve much like the man in the story, if we are dedicated to growing. As we do so, we breathe in the joy of our progressive accomplishments. We stay focused on the twelve step adage "One day at a time." We begin to see that accomplishment is not something that feeds our ego. It is not something that we are boastful about. Instead, accomplishment is the result of our willingness to gently ease into those parts of ourselves that we are afraid of.

*E*xercise: To shed the delusions of the addictive mind one has to *look within*. **Sit in silence for 15 minutes.** Look within by asking yourself:

- When have you been able to walk through a significant struggle?

- What accomplishments have we embraced in our lives?

- What praise have you received that has been difficult to accept?

❧

Notice how your body feels as you sit with these questions. For example, what are you feeling in your shoulders? In your arms? In your legs and feet? What emotions arise within? What thoughts come into your awareness? Give labels to your responses. "Shoulder tension," "sadness," "thinking," "anger," "frustration." Once labeled, bring your attention back to your breathing. Notice the rhythm of your breathing. If you find your attention drifting to other thoughts, label those thoughts briefly and bring your attention back to your breath.

When you have completed your meditation, reflect on what you became aware of and write them down on the next page. Include the emotions you felt. Share your reflection with the group and take note of their feedback. There is no right or wrong way to do this. You just simply need to do it.

Today's date: Days sober:

New Mind's Story:

Feelings that arose

	1 UNNOTICABLE	2	3	4	5 FLOODED
ANGER	1 UNNOTICABLE	2	3	4	5 FLOODED
FEAR	1 UNNOTICABLE	2	3	4	5 FLOODED
PAIN	1 UNNOTICABLE	2	3	4	5 FLOODED
JOY	1 UNNOTICABLE	2	3	4	5 FLOODED
PASSION	1 UNNOTICABLE	2	3	4	5 FLOODED
LOVE	1 UNNOTICABLE	2	3	4	5 FLOODED
SHAME	1 UNNOTICABLE	2	3	4	5 FLOODED
GUILT	1 UNNOTICABLE	2	3	4	5 FLOODED
OTHER:	1 UNNOTICABLE	2	3	4	5 FLOODED

Today's date:

Additional feedback:

What I learned about myself today...

One thing I can do to care for myself tonight...

Today's date: Days sober:

Day 22 Poison: **Isolation**

Ask the addictive mind:

- What does isolation mean to us?

- What would the consequences be if we chose isolation?

- How has isolation allowed us to grow?

Mind's Story:

Feelings that arose

ANGER	1 UNNOTICABLE	2	3	4	5 FLOODED
FEAR	1 UNNOTICABLE	2	3	4	5 FLOODED
PAIN	1 UNNOTICABLE	2	3	4	5 FLOODED
JOY	1 UNNOTICABLE	2	3	4	5 FLOODED
PASSION	1 UNNOTICABLE	2	3	4	5 FLOODED
LOVE	1 UNNOTICABLE	2	3	4	5 FLOODED
SHAME	1 UNNOTICABLE	2	3	4	5 FLOODED
GUILT	1 UNNOTICABLE	2	3	4	5 FLOODED
OTHER:	1 UNNOTICABLE	2	3	4	5 FLOODED

Feedback received

Discrepancies between *Feelings that Arose* and *Feedback Received?*

"In solitude, the mind gains

Day 22 Antidote: *Solitude*

I'm at another professional conference. My fellow therapists are milling about, talking about the latest therapies and books, each of them so seemingly joyful in their ability to connect. Their conversation illuminates their passion for our field. I, too, have these qualities. Yet in this room filled with so much knowledge, so much desire to help others, I feel totally and utterly alone.

How is it that we can feel so alone when we are surrounded by others? In addiction, we have split off part of our self. We do this to survive. We became so good at doing this, that even when we are in a room filled with friends or in a room with the love of our life, part of our self is out of that space. We have left parts that our mind deemed "undesirable" and tucked them away for no one to see, including ourselves.

In solitude, we rediscover parts of our self that laid outside awareness for some time. In solitude, we begin to reintegrate these parts which can only be done in a systematic manner. The first step is being present with the painful and shameful emotions that we have been attempting

strength and learns to lean upon itself."

—LAURENCE STRENE

to avoid. Though you may be tempted to dive right in, the key in this step is patience and gentleness.

Next, we must move close enough to these emotions that we gain the ability to tolerate them. Through tolerance, we can awaken to the wisdom those emotions have been trying to tell us. Slowly, we can share with those closest to us the parts of our self that have been isolated for so long, perhaps even a lifetime. The time for image control is in the past and progressively allowing all of ourselves to be seen by the world. This all begins with solitude.

The ancient Greek philosopher Pythagoras once said "Know thy self, and all the secrets of the universe shall be revealed." To know thy self, one must take time to connect with one's self. This is solitude—a step that frees us to be present emotionally with those around us. It is only through nurturing solitude that we begin to truly love not just others, but all of our self.

Exercise: To shed the delusions of the addictive mind one has to *look within*. **Sit in silence for 15 minutes.** Look within by asking yourself:

- Am I willing to make time for solitude?

❧

Notice how your body feels as you sit with these questions. For example, what are you feeling in your shoulders? In your arms? In your legs and feet? What emotions arise within? What thoughts come into your awareness? Give labels to your responses. "Shoulder tension," "sadness," "thinking," "anger," "frustration." Once labeled, bring your attention back to your breathing. Notice the rhythm of your breathing. If you find your attention drifting to other thoughts, label those thoughts briefly and bring your attention back to your breath.

When you have completed your meditation, reflect on what you became aware of and write them down on the next page. Include the emotions you felt. Share your reflection with the group and take note of their feedback. There is no right or wrong way to do this. You just simply need to do it.

Today's date: Days sober:

New Mind's Story:

Feelings that arose

	1	2	3	4	5
ANGER	UNNOTICABLE				FLOODED
FEAR	UNNOTICABLE				FLOODED
PAIN	UNNOTICABLE				FLOODED
JOY	UNNOTICABLE				FLOODED
PASSION	UNNOTICABLE				FLOODED
LOVE	UNNOTICABLE				FLOODED
SHAME	UNNOTICABLE				FLOODED
GUILT	UNNOTICABLE				FLOODED
OTHER:	UNNOTICABLE				FLOODED

Today's date:

Additional feedback:

What I learned about myself today...

One thing I can do to care for myself tonight...

Today's date: Days sober:

Day 23 Poison: **Cynicism**

Ask the addictive mind:

- What are we cynical about?

- What purpose does our cynical outlook serve?

M*ind's Story:*

Feelings that arose

	1 UNNOTICABLE	2	3	4	5 FLOODED
ANGER	1 UNNOTICABLE	2	3	4	5 FLOODED
FEAR	1 UNNOTICABLE	2	3	4	5 FLOODED
PAIN	1 UNNOTICABLE	2	3	4	5 FLOODED
JOY	1 UNNOTICABLE	2	3	4	5 FLOODED
PASSION	1 UNNOTICABLE	2	3	4	5 FLOODED
LOVE	1 UNNOTICABLE	2	3	4	5 FLOODED
SHAME	1 UNNOTICABLE	2	3	4	5 FLOODED
GUILT	1 UNNOTICABLE	2	3	4	5 FLOODED
OTHER:	1 UNNOTICABLE	2	3	4	5 FLOODED

Feedback received

Discrepancies between *Feelings that Arose* and *Feedback Received?*

"The heroic soul does not sell

Day 23 Antidote: *Nobleness*

Often times we see or read the news and have strong emotional reactions to tragic or unsettling events. We can feel overwhelmed by the latest act of terrorism, mass shooting, or progressive climate change that could end all life on the planet. It is no wonder that popular Western culture is saturated with cynicism. What can we do?

Change in the world starts with just one person. It starts with one thought or action. The Buddha, Christ, and Mohammed were all influential people who changed our world. They did not start off by declaring that they would change the world for the better. Each day, they simply aligned with the change they wanted to see. They conducted themselves in a loving, compassionate, and gentle way. They were respectful to all people they encountered, and people gravitated towards them because of it.

Being a loving, compassionate, and gentle person does not mean you have to drop everything and start a charity, do volunteer work, or enroll as a missionary. These are all great things, but greatness can also come from a collection of small things. Something as simple as a

it's justice and it's nobleness."

—RALPH WALDO EMERSON

smile, holding the elevator door, or saying "good morning" can make a person's day. These are things that we have the choice to do or not do. These are the small things that can lead to great personal change. When we resist the urge to be cynical and instead become a conduit for kindness and respect, a seed of nobleness is planted within, and with time can replace the cynicism of the addictive mind.

*E*xercise: To shed the delusions of the addictive mind one has to *look within*. **Sit in silence for 15 minutes.** Look within by asking yourself:

- How can I grow the seed of nobleness?

&

Notice how your body feels as you sit with these questions. For example, what are you feeling in your shoulders? In your arms? In your legs and feet? What emotions arise within? What thoughts come into your awareness? Give labels to your responses. "Shoulder tension," "sadness," "thinking," "anger," "frustration." Once labeled, bring your attention back to your breathing. Notice the rhythm of your breathing. If you find your attention drifting to other thoughts, label those thoughts briefly and bring your attention back to your breath.

When you have completed your meditation, reflect on what you became aware of and write them down on the next page. Include the emotions you felt. Share your reflection with the group and take note of their feedback. There is no right or wrong way to do this. You just simply need to do it.

Today's date: Days sober:

New Mind's Story:

Feelings that arose

	1 UNNOTICABLE	2	3	4	5 FLOODED
ANGER	1 UNNOTICABLE	2	3	4	5 FLOODED
FEAR	1 UNNOTICABLE	2	3	4	5 FLOODED
PAIN	1 UNNOTICABLE	2	3	4	5 FLOODED
JOY	1 UNNOTICABLE	2	3	4	5 FLOODED
PASSION	1 UNNOTICABLE	2	3	4	5 FLOODED
LOVE	1 UNNOTICABLE	2	3	4	5 FLOODED
SHAME	1 UNNOTICABLE	2	3	4	5 FLOODED
GUILT	1 UNNOTICABLE	2	3	4	5 FLOODED
OTHER:	1 UNNOTICABLE	2	3	4	5 FLOODED

Today's date:

Additional feedback:

.

What I learned about myself today...

One thing I can do to care for myself tonight...

Today's date: Days sober:

Day 24 Poison: **Reproach**

Ask the addictive mind:

- In what ways am I critical of you?

- How does negative judgment leave you empowered?

Mind's Story:

Feelings that arose

	1 UNNOTICABLE	2	3	4	5 FLOODED
ANGER	1	2	3	4	5
FEAR	1	2	3	4	5
PAIN	1	2	3	4	5
JOY	1	2	3	4	5
PASSION	1	2	3	4	5
LOVE	1	2	3	4	5
SHAME	1	2	3	4	5
GUILT	1	2	3	4	5
OTHER:	1	2	3	4	5

Feedback received

Discrepancies between *Feelings that Arose* and *Feedback Received?*

"What you praise

Day 24 Antidote: *Praise*

It is so important in our relationships to voice our needs, whether it be from friends, family, our significant other, or ourselves. Voicing our needs does not come easily. Some avoid it all together. Take praise, for example. Everyone enjoys being praised or acknowledged for certain things they have done, even if they pretend or believe that they don't. It's in our nature to desire validation and appreciation. If we don't receive it or ask for it, we may feel sad, disappointed, or resentful.

Of course, asking for acknowledgement or positive feedback from others places you in a vulnerable position. You could be let down and receive criticism rather than praise. On the other hand, you could receive what you need—acknowledgement for your deeds, which would counter the self-doubts festering in your mind's story. This is not about inflating one's ego. A common misconception about praise is that its value is diminished the more it is given, that the person receiving the praise will become "used to it" or come to "expect it." Praise is not the same as flattery which is overstated for effect. It is about taking care of yourself and building your self-respect.

you increase."

—CATHERINE PONDER

It is also important that we give praise or credit to those we love. Do you praise people, or yourself, for successes or for the small things done well? Sincerely giving praise is about letting others or yourself know that they are loved and appreciated, which ultimately increases the fulfillment of our relationships.

*E*xercise: To shed the delusions of the addictive mind one has to *look within*. **Sit in silence for 15 minutes.** Look within by asking yourself:

- Am I willing and open to accept praise?

- Am I willing and open to give praise to myself and others?

ᵱ

Notice how your body feels as you sit with these questions. For example, what are you feeling in your shoulders? In your arms? In your legs and feet? What emotions arise within? What thoughts come into your awareness? Give labels to your responses. "Shoulder tension," "sadness," "thinking," "anger," "frustration." Once labeled, bring your attention back to your breathing. Notice the rhythm of your breathing. If you find your attention drifting to other thoughts, label those thoughts briefly and bring your attention back to your breath.

When you have completed your meditation, reflect on what you became aware of and write them down on the next page. Include the emotions you felt. Share your reflection with the group and take note of their feedback. There is no right or wrong way to do this. You just simply need to do it.

Today's date: Days sober:

New Mind's Story:

Feelings that arose

	1	2	3	4	5
ANGER	UNNOTICABLE				FLOODED
FEAR	UNNOTICABLE				FLOODED
PAIN	UNNOTICABLE				FLOODED
JOY	UNNOTICABLE				FLOODED
PASSION	UNNOTICABLE				FLOODED
LOVE	UNNOTICABLE				FLOODED
SHAME	UNNOTICABLE				FLOODED
GUILT	UNNOTICABLE				FLOODED
OTHER:	UNNOTICABLE				FLOODED

Today's date:

Additional feedback:

What I learned about myself today...

One thing I can do to care for myself tonight...

Day 25 Poison: **Stagnation**

Ask the addictive mind:

- Have we found recovery to be stagnant?

- What barriers do we still have in recovery?

Mind's Story:

Feelings that arose

ANGER	*1* *UNNOTICABLE*	*2*	*3*	*4*	*5* *FLOODED*
FEAR	*1* *UNNOTICABLE*	*2*	*3*	*4*	*5* *FLOODED*
PAIN	*1* *UNNOTICABLE*	*2*	*3*	*4*	*5* *FLOODED*
JOY	*1* *UNNOTICABLE*	*2*	*3*	*4*	*5* *FLOODED*
PASSION	*1* *UNNOTICABLE*	*2*	*3*	*4*	*5* *FLOODED*
LOVE	*1* *UNNOTICABLE*	*2*	*3*	*4*	*5* *FLOODED*
SHAME	*1* *UNNOTICABLE*	*2*	*3*	*4*	*5* *FLOODED*
GUILT	*1* *UNNOTICABLE*	*2*	*3*	*4*	*5* *FLOODED*
OTHER:	*1* *UNNOTICABLE*	*2*	*3*	*4*	*5* *FLOODED*

Feedback received

Discrepancies between *Feelings that Arose* and *Feedback Received?*

"Energy cannot be created

Day 25 Antidote: *Living in Reality*

Some people say that life is just a wild ride that ends with you shriveled up, gray, and sliding into a grave. Others say life is precious and that one should be humble and gentle when exiting this world. The two points of views are polar opposites, but both have merit. Living in reality is about being present in the infinite plane of possibility. The only truth is that each moment is unknown.

Every moment the mind creates a thought construct or an emotional energy that becomes a statement that something is *this* or something is *that*. The truth is none of *this* or *that* is, in fact, real. In reality, all things are in a constant state of change. The mind is simply a process, a cacophony of cellular interactions which is without end until the day we pass. We have the choice to simply notice that process or react to it. Energy cannot be created or destroyed. It merely changes form. This energy is how we sustain our bodily function and ability to express ourselves in our three-dimensional universe.

Awareness of that expression is aligned with the truth of constant change. It is only when we realize that death, birth, and living are all

or destroyed. It can only
be transformed."
—2ND LAW OF CONSERVATION OF ENERGY

processes we will no longer suffer or fear. When we realize the leading cause of death is birth or life, fearing death becomes unnecessary. Whether you view life as a wild ride, a precious journey, or both, at the core of it all, we are all energy that cannot be created or destroyed; we can only change form.

*E*xercise: To shed the delusions of the addictive mind one has to *look within*. **Sit in silence for 15 minutes.** Look within by asking yourself:

- How am I embracing the process of change?

Notice how your body feels as you sit with these questions. For example, what are you feeling in your shoulders? In your arms? In your legs and feet? What emotions arise within? What thoughts come into your awareness? Give labels to your responses. "Shoulder tension," "sadness," "thinking," "anger," "frustration." Once labeled, bring your attention back to your breathing. Notice the rhythm of your breathing. If you find your attention drifting to other thoughts, label those thoughts briefly and bring your attention back to your breath.

When you have completed your meditation, reflect on what you became aware of and write them down on the next page. Include the emotions you felt. Share your reflection with the group and take note of their feedback. There is no right or wrong way to do this. You just simply need to do it.

Today's date: Days sober:

*N*ew Mind's Story:

Feelings that arose

	UNNOTICABLE				FLOODED
ANGER	1	2	3	4	5
FEAR	1	2	3	4	5
PAIN	1	2	3	4	5
JOY	1	2	3	4	5
PASSION	1	2	3	4	5
LOVE	1	2	3	4	5
SHAME	1	2	3	4	5
GUILT	1	2	3	4	5
OTHER:	1	2	3	4	5

Today's date:

Additional feedback:

What I learned about myself today...

One thing I can do to care for myself tonight...

Today's date: Days sober:

Day 26 Poison: **Despair**

Ask the addictive mind:

- What was the last crisis that drove us to despair?

Mind's Story:

Feelings that arose

	1 UNNOTICABLE	2	3	4	5 FLOODED
ANGER	1 UNNOTICABLE	2	3	4	5 FLOODED
FEAR	1 UNNOTICABLE	2	3	4	5 FLOODED
PAIN	1 UNNOTICABLE	2	3	4	5 FLOODED
JOY	1 UNNOTICABLE	2	3	4	5 FLOODED
PASSION	1 UNNOTICABLE	2	3	4	5 FLOODED
LOVE	1 UNNOTICABLE	2	3	4	5 FLOODED
SHAME	1 UNNOTICABLE	2	3	4	5 FLOODED
GUILT	1 UNNOTICABLE	2	3	4	5 FLOODED
OTHER:	1 UNNOTICABLE	2	3	4	5 FLOODED

Feedback received

Discrepancies between *Feelings that Arose* and *Feedback Received?*

"I dug a hole and buried myself

Day 26 Antidote: *Surrender*

When Joe got his second DUI charge and lost his job of 10 years selling insurance, he went through the five stages of grieving. At first, he was in denial. Surely a good lawyer could argue that the breathalyzer wasn't calibrated, which would throw out his blood alcohol reading.

He was angry and blamed the insurance company. He believed they encouraged his drinking from the many office-paid happy hours. He contemplated bargaining with one of the head managers and even called him. After some awkward small talk, however, he could not bring himself to ask for a third chance. After all, he hated the job and wished he was working somewhere that allowed for creativity.

He began to binge drink, relishing in what he considered his rightful despair, but after a few weeks, he found he could no longer reach oblivion. He added other substances into the mix, hoping it would help, but that made things worse. In the meantime, his sister, aware of his situation, encouraged him to go into rehab while he still had health insurance. One morning, sick of trying to make it work on his own, he conceded and checked into an outpatient treatment program.

After some months, he found himself working in the back of a café as a baker. It was the only place that would take him after reviewing his background check. He found that working in a kitchen could be a creative

this seed-like knot I'd become, and waited for rain."

—VADDEY RATNER

endeavor. He threw himself into his work, decorating cakes and cookies and within a few months he was promoted to head baker. He attended 12-step meetings for his drinking. Months went by, and he realized one day that he was no longer miserable. He was doing something he did not mind, and at times, enjoyed. All of which might not have happened were it not for the loss of his job at the insurance company.

છે

Being able to acknowledge and walk through moments of loss, despair or confusion and finding support and hope from others on the journey of recovery is something Joe had to go through to get to a better place. Escaping his pain through binge drinking kept him static, unemployed, and stuck in the chaos of losing a job he depended on.

Loss and opportunity go hand-in-hand. Every loss warrants a decision-something new and expansive, a chance to morph the human psyche toward hope, growth, and serenity. Someimes the loss can be so consuming that the idea of opportunity does not exist in conciousness. Sometimes it takes surrendering your own thought process and listening to the suggestions from loved ones for the opportunity to make itself known.

*E*xercise: To shed the delusions of the addictive mind one has to *look within*. **Sit in silence for 15 minutes.** Look within by asking yourself:

- What gains have I had from certain losses in my life?

- Am I willing to seek and accept surrender to overcome despair?

🙢

Notice how your body feels as you sit with these questions. For example, what are you feeling in your shoulders? In your arms? In your legs and feet? What emotions arise within? What thoughts come into your awareness? Give labels to your responses. "Shoulder tension," "sadness," "thinking," "anger," "frustration." Once labeled, bring your attention back to your breathing. Notice the rhythm of your breathing. If you find your attention drifting to other thoughts, label those thoughts briefly and bring your attention back to your breath.

When you have completed your meditation, reflect on what you became aware of and write them down on the next page. Include the emotions you felt. Share your reflection with the group and take note of their feedback. There is no right or wrong way to do this. You just simply need to do it.

Day 26: Despair ❧ Surrender

Today's date: Days sober:

New Mind's Story:

Feelings that arose

	1	2	3	4	5
ANGER	UNNOTICABLE				FLOODED
FEAR	UNNOTICABLE				FLOODED
PAIN	UNNOTICABLE				FLOODED
JOY	UNNOTICABLE				FLOODED
PASSION	UNNOTICABLE				FLOODED
LOVE	UNNOTICABLE				FLOODED
SHAME	UNNOTICABLE				FLOODED
GUILT	UNNOTICABLE				FLOODED
OTHER:	UNNOTICABLE				FLOODED

Day 26: Despair & Surrender

Today's date:

Additional feedback:

What I learned about myself today...

One thing I can do to care for myself tonight...

Today's date: Days sober:

Day 27 Poison: **Impulsivity**

Ask the addictive mind:

- How has our impulsivity contributed to the negative consequences of our lives?

- How has acting on our whims affected those around us?

Mind's Story:

Feelings that arose

ANGER		1	2	3	4	5
		UNNOTICABLE				FLOODED

FEAR		1	2	3	4	5
		UNNOTICABLE				FLOODED

PAIN		1	2	3	4	5
		UNNOTICABLE				FLOODED

JOY		1	2	3	4	5
		UNNOTICABLE				FLOODED

PASSION		1	2	3	4	5
		UNNOTICABLE				FLOODED

LOVE		1	2	3	4	5
		UNNOTICABLE				FLOODED

SHAME		1	2	3	4	5
		UNNOTICABLE				FLOODED

GUILT		1	2	3	4	5
		UNNOTICABLE				FLOODED

OTHER:		1	2	3	4	5
		UNNOTICABLE				FLOODED

Feedback received

Discrepancies between *Feelings that Arose* and *Feedback Received?*

"Go wisely and go slowly.

Day 27 Antidote: *Wisdom*

On a rainy day, a frog decided to cross the river. A scorpion approached the frog and asked seductively, "May you carry me across the river?"

The frog hestitated with fear, knowing that the scorpion had a reputation for fatal stinging. The frog said to the scorpion, "No way, what do you think I am, *stupid*? You could sting me!"

The scorpion argued back, "That doesn't make any sense. Why would I sting you? If I sting you while we're crossing the river, we'll both drown. I don't want to die."

The frog considered this and thought to himself, "That makes sense. Why would the scorpion want to die? He wouldn't." So the frog agreed.

Midway across the river, the frog felt a sharp pinch on his back. "Ouch," the frog said. "You stung me? Now we're both going to die! Why did you sting me?"
The scorpion replied, "I can't help myself. It is my nature."

❦

In recovery, we will run into people, places, and things that we know are our personal scorpions. It is important to keep in mind that despite

Those who rush stumble and fall." —SHAKESPEARE

having some time of sobriety, addiction is like the scorpion. We may be swayed to go down a path that leads us to the same fate the frog met.

It is the addictive mind's nature to lead you down a path of self-deception and destruction. It is in its nature to trick you into believing things will be different, or not the way you know them to be. This is what wisdom is not. You will encounter the thoughts the addictive mind projects throughout the day. They may not be loud or profoundly effecting, they may not be intensely disregulating, but they will always be false.

When encountering them, utilize introspection. Ask yourself, *What am I feeling? What feeling is the addictive mind trying to distract me from? Do I need to ask for help?* By reflecting on what the addictive mind is trying to convey, wisdom can be gleaned.

*E*xercise: To shed the delusions of the addictive mind one has to *look within*. **Sit in silence for 15 minutes.** Look within by asking yourself:

- How is my wise-mind currently helping me to overcome the seduction of the addictive mind (scorpion)?

Notice how your body feels as you sit with these questions. For example, what are you feeling in your shoulders? In your arms? In your legs and feet? What emotions arise within? What thoughts come into your awareness? Give labels to your responses. "Shoulder tension," "sadness," "thinking," "anger," "frustration." Once labeled, bring your attention back to your breathing. Notice the rhythm of your breathing. If you find your attention drifting to other thoughts, label those thoughts briefly and bring your attention back to your breath.

When you have completed your meditation, reflect on what you became aware of and write them down on the next page. Include the emotions you felt. Share your reflection with the group and take note of their feedback. There is no right or wrong way to do this. You just simply need to do it.

Today's date: Days sober:

New Mind's Story:

Feelings that arose

	1	2	3	4	5
ANGER	UNNOTICABLE				FLOODED
FEAR	UNNOTICABLE				FLOODED
PAIN	UNNOTICABLE				FLOODED
JOY	UNNOTICABLE				FLOODED
PASSION	UNNOTICABLE				FLOODED
LOVE	UNNOTICABLE				FLOODED
SHAME	UNNOTICABLE				FLOODED
GUILT	UNNOTICABLE				FLOODED
OTHER:	UNNOTICABLE				FLOODED

Today's date:

Additional feedback:

What I learned about myself today...

One thing I can do to care for myself tonight...

Today's date: Days sober:

Day 28 Poison: **Procrastination**

Ask the addictive mind:

- What deadlines or duties do we push aside?

- What stories are you telling me to justify putting things off?

Mind's Story:

Feelings that arose

	1	2	3	4	5
ANGER	UNNOTICABLE				FLOODED
FEAR	UNNOTICABLE				FLOODED
PAIN	UNNOTICABLE				FLOODED
JOY	UNNOTICABLE				FLOODED
PASSION	UNNOTICABLE				FLOODED
LOVE	UNNOTICABLE				FLOODED
SHAME	UNNOTICABLE				FLOODED
GUILT	UNNOTICABLE				FLOODED
OTHER:	UNNOTICABLE				FLOODED

Feedback received

Discrepancies between *Feelings that Arose* and *Feedback Received?*

"Pure love is a willingness

Day 28 Antidote: *Willingness*

When Charles ripped open his Uncle Kevin's graduation present, his face fell. Then he began to laugh. Surely this was a joke. He was expecting money. Everyone else's presents came short, but he knew his Uncle Kevin would come through. He never disappointed him when it came to kindness and generosity. He looked around to see if he had missed any other packages, but there were none left unopened.

When he realized it wasn't a joke, Charles became irate. Not only were his expectations disappointed, but to add insult to injury, the gift he received was a tourist's guide to Santa Barbara, the city where he would be attending university in the Fall. He considered himself well versed in what the city had to offer, having searched the internet for all the local bars, restaurants and popular hang-out spots that sparked his interest. *Why would I ever need to read this?* he wondered. Should he get lost in the city, which he believed was highly unlikely, he would find directions through electronic means, not an antiquated book. After staring at the back cover and briefly fanning the book, he tossed it aside and forgot about it.

In the fall, Charles packed up his things and went away for his first year in college. On one of his visits home for the holidays, he stumbled across the tourist guide his uncle had given him. He picked it up and

to give without a thought to receiving anything in return." —PEACE PILGRIM

fanned through the pages again, wondering how much it was worth and if he could sell it online. As he went through the book, he stopped here and there to skim over possible hiking trails and other destinations he was not aware of. As he did so, a giftcard fell from one of the tucked away, folded maps. He went online to check the balance on the giftcard. To his disbelief, the amount was more than he had hoped for.

*E*xercise: To shed the delusions of the addictive mind one has to *look within*. **Sit in silence for 15 minutes.** Look within by asking yourself:

- What rewards might have been gained if you were willing to accept something the addictive mind said it didn't want?

❦

Notice how your body feels as you sit with these questions. For example, what are you feeling in your shoulders? In your arms? In your legs and feet? What emotions arise within? What thoughts come into your awareness? Give labels to your responses. "Shoulder tension," "sadness," "thinking," "anger," "frustration." Once labeled, bring your attention back to your breathing. Notice the rhythm of your breathing. If you find your attention drifting to other thoughts, label those thoughts briefly and bring your attention back to your breath.

When you have completed your meditation, reflect on what you became aware of and write them down on the next page. Include the emotions you felt. Share your reflection with the group and take note of their feedback. There is no right or wrong way to do this. You just simply need to do it.

Today's date: Days sober:

New Mind's Story:

Feelings that arose

	1	2	3	4	5
ANGER	*UNNOTICABLE*	2	3	4	*FLOODED*
FEAR	*UNNOTICABLE*	2	3	4	*FLOODED*
PAIN	*UNNOTICABLE*	2	3	4	*FLOODED*
JOY	*UNNOTICABLE*	2	3	4	*FLOODED*
PASSION	*UNNOTICABLE*	2	3	4	*FLOODED*
LOVE	*UNNOTICABLE*	2	3	4	*FLOODED*
SHAME	*UNNOTICABLE*	2	3	4	*FLOODED*
GUILT	*UNNOTICABLE*	2	3	4	*FLOODED*
OTHER:	*UNNOTICABLE*	2	3	4	*FLOODED*

Today's date:

Additional feedback:

What I learned about myself today...

One thing I can do to care for myself tonight...

Today's date: Days sober:

Day 29 Poison: **Apathy**

Ask the addictive mind:

- What are the ways we are refusing to extinguish our indifference towards each other?

Mind's Story:

Feelings that arose

	1	2	3	4	5
ANGER	UNNOTICABLE				FLOODED
FEAR	UNNOTICABLE				FLOODED
PAIN	UNNOTICABLE				FLOODED
JOY	UNNOTICABLE				FLOODED
PASSION	UNNOTICABLE				FLOODED
LOVE	UNNOTICABLE				FLOODED
SHAME	UNNOTICABLE				FLOODED
GUILT	UNNOTICABLE				FLOODED
OTHER:	UNNOTICABLE				FLOODED

Feedback received

Discrepancies between *Feelings that Arose* and *Feedback Received?*

"We can only keep what

Day 29 Antidote: *Empathy*

It had just passed 2 a.m. when Michael's phone rang. He was glad for the interruption. For the past ½ hour, he had been looking fruitlessly for lecture notes he needed to finish his paper. He saw the caller had a familar 212 number and thought it was his friend Shane.

He was surprised to hear a woman's voice on the line. Michael didn't really want to finish his paper and his curiosity was sparked, so he decided to talk to her *for a bit* and see where things went. *She might even be cute,* he thought.

Talking "for a bit" turned into an hour, and before long, Michael saw the sun coming up. He talked very little. The woman who had the wrong number had much to get off her chest. He didn't mind because he could relate to her story of trying to end a long-term relationship that had become destructive. He also related to her struggles with drinking—how she would throw the half-empty liquor bottle in the trash in the morning before work only to pick it out at night when she couldn't sleep.

When the woman was done telling her story, she asked him what she should do. Michael became worried. He didn't know what to say. He wanted to say something meaningful, something comforting, and he felt like if he didn't come up with something, he would be letting her down. The caller was silent. After a time, Michael said the only truthful thing

we have by giving it away."

—NARCOTICS ANONYMOUS

he could say. "I'm not sure who you meant to call, but I don't think it was me. I'm sure we haven't met."

The caller was stunned in silence for a moment. When she spoke again, she said she meant to call her 12-step sponsor. She asked him why he didn't interrupt her and say anything? Michael replied, "It sounded like you really needed someone to hear you out. I'm sorry you are going through this. I can relate to what you shared..."

Michael could have spoken up, told the caller she had the wrong number and went back to his business. Instead, he chose to be present with her. Despite his initial intentions, he heard someone in pain. He decided to listen, allowing the caller the space to be heard. He found himself having empathy for her as she spoke of scenarios that were all too familar to him. Sometimes we don't need to say a thing to give comfort to someone else. Sometimes choosing to be present and actively listenning can be the best thing we can do for someone else.

*E*xercise: To shed the delusions of the addictive mind one has to *look within*. **Sit in silence for 15 minutes.** Look within by asking yourself:

- In what ways can we embrace empathy in our lives?

Notice how your body feels as you sit with these questions. For example, what are you feeling in your shoulders? In your arms? In your legs and feet? What emotions arise within? What thoughts come into your awareness? Give labels to your responses. "Shoulder tension," "sadness," "thinking," "anger," "frustration." Once labeled, bring your attention back to your breathing. Notice the rhythm of your breathing. If you find your attention drifting to other thoughts, label those thoughts briefly and bring your attention back to your breath.

When you have completed your meditation, reflect on what you became aware of and write them down on the next page. Include the emotions you felt. Share your reflection with the group and take note of their feedback. There is no right or wrong way to do this. You just simply need to do it.

Today's date: Days sober:

New Mind's Story:

Feelings that arose

ANGER		1 UNNOTICABLE	2	3	4	5 FLOODED

FEAR		1 UNNOTICABLE	2	3	4	5 FLOODED

PAIN		1 UNNOTICABLE	2	3	4	5 FLOODED

JOY		1 UNNOTICABLE	2	3	4	5 FLOODED

PASSION	UNNOTICABLE	1	2	3	4	5 FLOODED

LOVE		1 UNNOTICABLE	2	3	4	5 FLOODED

SHAME		1 UNNOTICABLE	2	3	4	5 FLOODED

GUILT		1 UNNOTICABLE	2	3	4	5 FLOODED

OTHER:		1 UNNOTICABLE	2	3	4	5 FLOODED

Today's date:

Additional feedback:

What I learned about myself today...

One thing I can do to care for myself tonight...

Day 30 Poison: **Control**

Ask the addictive mind:

- How controlling are we of our image?

- What do we get through image control?

Mind's Story:

Feelings that arose

	1	2	3	4	5
ANGER	UNNOTICABLE				FLOODED
FEAR	UNNOTICABLE				FLOODED
PAIN	UNNOTICABLE				FLOODED
JOY	UNNOTICABLE				FLOODED
PASSION	UNNOTICABLE				FLOODED
LOVE	UNNOTICABLE				FLOODED
SHAME	UNNOTICABLE				FLOODED
GUILT	UNNOTICABLE				FLOODED
OTHER:	UNNOTICABLE				FLOODED

Feedback received

Discrepancies between *Feelings that Arose* and *Feedback Received?*

"If I show it to you now

Day 30 Antidote: *Vulnerability*

The sun beat down on the white decorative rocks that filled the front yard of the pale blue double-wide trailer. You could see the four-foot high fence baking in the 120 degree heat. Mid-July in the Mojave Desert. It can be literally the hottest place on the planet. I sat in my car, flooded again with rage, pain, and a deep sorrow. At age 19 I was still a senior in high school. I had been held back in 2nd grade due to my dyslexia, and thus was one to two years older than my classmates.

I turned my car off and wiped the tears from my face. I went up to the white door and knocked. She quickly answered, and I was greeted with her wonderful, loving smile. It was my great Aunt Loraine who was the around 65 years old. She was retired. Everything about her would tell you she was a conservative woman. She was the widow of a Navy Admiral who commanded the Pacific Fleet. Now, however, she was alone in the Mojave Valley, Arizona, the other side of the Colorado river from where I lived.

My school had a total of 300 students. My graduating class was 60 kids. It was the late '80's, President Ronald Reagan ran the show. I lived in the heart of "Reagan" country. Suffice to say where I grew up, there was no room for anyone other than white heterosexual men and women.

At any rate, Aunt Lorraine invited me in, and offered me water and a

will it make you run away?" —KELLY CLARKSON

chair. Our talks usually consisted of me crying, telling her I was so upset because my best friend Ben was giving attention to our other friends. Sometimes, he would not go out with me, leaving me feeling betrayed and hurt. Anger would overwhelm me, and I could speak to no one about it except my Aunt Loraine. On this day I was particularly vexed and could not understand why I was so upset.

I sat and spoke with her for about an hour, and I decided to take a risk and share with her something I had wondered about myself but could never bring myself to say to anyone, including myself. I thought that maybe I was gay. Should I should ask her? Then this domineering, intimidating voice would drown the thoughts in my head.

NO, NO, Don't ever bring anything like that up. Are you crazy? You would be killed, and after all, you know God can forgive murder, but he cannot forgive Gays. What if your friends found out? They would beat you up; you could be thrown out of your house. Your mom and dad would stop talking to you. You would lose your sister, and she would never let you see your nieces again. NO, NO, think how you would embarrass everyone in your family. NO, you are not gay. You are just messed up. It will pass. Whatever you do, don't ask her!

This day, the pain was too much. I needed to be seen and heard, this part of myself that had been locked away in a dark room its whole life needed to be witnessed. So there I was sitting in my chair and I said, "Aunt Rain?" She responded with, "Yes, Honey?" I then looked at her, and in a very low voice , as my eyes veered toward the ground and my hands went into my lap, I asked, "Do you think I might be gay?" I was not prepared for her response. She looked at me with pure joy in her face, with her amazing smile, and said, "Oh, honey, I am so glad you finally said it! I was here thinking day after day, 'If I could just get him to say it, we could talk about it!' I want you to know that if you are gay, I love you and nothing would ever change that."

I felt invigorated and stunned. I said a little louder, "Yeah, I think I am gay." She stood up and gave me a big hug. I began to cry which turned to sobs, then wails. I cried for a very long time. I realized that moment I had chosen the courage to be vulnerable. In that moment I had allowed myself to be seen, all of myself, not just the parts I felt would be acceptable. In that moment, there in the living room of that trailer with my Aunt holding me, I knew I was loved--not for what I thought others would love me for, but for who I was. This was the first time I ever came out of the closet to anyone. Even myself.

Day 30: Vulnerability

❦

If I had been able to align with vulnerability much sooner, the pain and suffering I was going through could have been dramatically reduced. This is the great lie the addictive mind tells us; that if we somehow continue to hide those parts of our self we think are unlovable, that it won't hurt us. The reality is the more we hide, the less vulnerable we are, resulting in a greater sense of isolation and loneliness. As a result, we tell ourselves we must be unlovable, and the spiral continues until we wake up one day and realize we are alone. The cure for addiction is connection; the only way to gain connection is to be vulnerable.

*E*xercise: To shed the delusions of the addictive mind, one has to *look within*. **Sit in silence for 15 minutes.** Look within by asking yourself:

- How can I know I am loved if I don't allow all of myself to be present?

Notice how your body feels as you sit with these questions. For example, what are you feeling in your shoulders? In your arms? In your legs and feet? What emotions arise within? What thoughts come into your awareness? Give labels to your responses. "Shoulder tension," "sadness," "thinking," "anger," "frustration." Once labeled, bring your attention back to your breathing. Notice the rhythm of your breathing. If you find your attention drifting to other thoughts, label those thoughts briefly and bring your attention back to your breath.

When you have completed your meditation, reflect on what you became aware of and write them down on the next page. Include the emotions you felt. Share your reflection with the group and take note of their feedback. There is no right or wrong way to do this. You just simply need to do it.

Day 30: Control & Vulnerability

Today's date: Days sober:

New Mind's Story:

Feelings that arose

	1	2	3	4	5
ANGER	UNNOTICABLE				FLOODED
FEAR	UNNOTICABLE				FLOODED
PAIN	UNNOTICABLE				FLOODED
JOY	UNNOTICABLE				FLOODED
PASSION	UNNOTICABLE				FLOODED
LOVE	UNNOTICABLE				FLOODED
SHAME	UNNOTICABLE				FLOODED
GUILT	UNNOTICABLE				FLOODED
OTHER:	UNNOTICABLE				FLOODED

Today's date:

Additional feedback:

What I learned about myself today...

One thing I can do to care for myself tonight...

Days 21 - 30 Summary

Directions: Look for Worksheet C at the end of this book. Cut it out and return to this page. Review Feelings that Arose worksheets for the previous 10 days. You quantified your feelings twice per day--once after Ask the Addictive Mind and again after meditating. Add up the total number of points for each emotion from these worksheets. Shade in your result. The left side of each collumn should reflect the summation from Ask the Addictive Mind. The right side of the collumn reflects the summation after meditating.

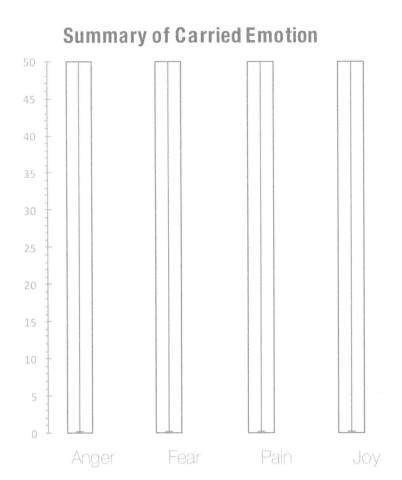

Summary of Carried Emotion

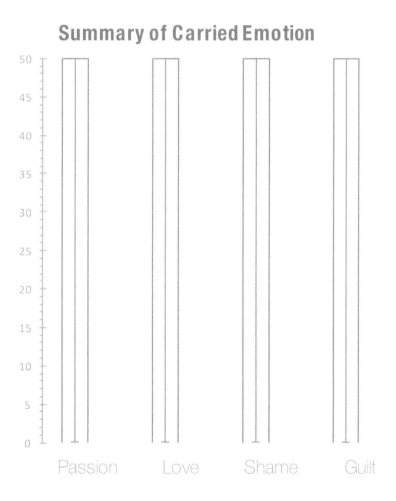

Summary of Carried Emotion

WORKSHEET A: FIRST TEN DAYS' EMOTION

DAY	ANGER		FEAR		PAIN		JOY		PASSION		LOVE		SHAME		GUILT	
	A	M	A	M	A	M	A	M	A	M	A	M	A	M	A	M
1																
2																
3																
4																
5																
6																
7																
8																
9																
10																
TOTAL																

If you have fully completed ten days, you would have ranked your emotions twenty times (twice per day): once after *Ask the Addictive Mind* (A) and again after meditating (M). Record those ratings on this sheet. Add up the ratings and return to the Emotions Summary page where you will shade in each sum. By doing this, you will have a visual on the intensity of your emotions over the past ten days.

WORKSHEET B: DAYS 11 - 20

DAY	ANGER		FEAR		PAIN		JOY		PASSION		LOVE		SHAME		GUILT	
	A	M	A	M	A	M	A	M	A	M	A	M	A	M	A	M
1																
2																
3																
4																
5																
6																
7																
8																
9																
10																
TOTAL																

For days 11 - 20, Record the ratings of your emotions on this sheet. Add up the ratings and return to the Emotions Summary page where you will shade in each sum. By doing this, you will have a visual on the intensity of your emotions over the past ten days.

WORKSHEET C: DAYS 21 - 30

DAY	ANGER		FEAR		PAIN		JOY		PASSION		LOVE		SHAME		GUILT	
	A	M	A	M	A	M	A	M	A	M	A	M	A	M	A	M
1																
2																
3																
4																
5																
6																
7																
8																
9																
10																
TOTAL																

For days 21 - 30, Record the ratings of your emotions on this sheet. Add up the ratings and return to the Emotions Summary page where you will shade in each sum. By doing this, you will have a visual on the intensity of your emotions over the past ten days.

About Darrin Ford

Darrin Ford is a licensed Marriage and Family Therapist specializing in treating addictive disorders. His practice began in Long Beach, California and has extended over the years to include treatment centers in West Los Angeles and Orange County. As founder of Mindful Centers for Addiction and Trauma Therapy (mindfulcenters.com), he serves as the chief executive officer, runs intensive workshops, and mentors new therapists. He is certified as a clinical supervisor by the American Association of Marriage and Family Therapists. He is also certified as a Sex Addiction Therapist, and was directly trained directly by the pioneer of the field, Dr. Patrick Carnes.

In his years of treating those afflicted with addiction, he ascertained the keystone of mindfulness in breaking free from old patterns, habits, and ways of thinking. Steeped in his passion for science and Buddhist philosophy, he founded the Mindfulness-Based Addiction & Trauma Therapy Certification Program (MBATT™) which is run through The Mindfulness Academy for Addiction & Trauma Training (tmaatt.com). His expertise in the field of addictive behaviors can be found in the program, which takes a modern approach to Eastern techniques in exploring the mind.

His part-memoir, part self-help book, *Awakening from the Sexually Addicted Mind: A Guide to Compassionate Recovery*, sheds an intimate light on his own struggles and how he came to help others on a path he is intimately familiar with. His book is available now in print through Sanopress.com or in Kindle format on Amazon.com.

Untitled

When I die, I want to be ready.
I don't want there to be any *I'm sorry's*
that I didn't say.
I don't want there to be any space
for regret of the things I did not try.
I don't want there to be chances
that I was too afraid to take.

When I die, I want to have tried it all
and grown from the experiences.
I want to have failed.
I want to have succeeded.
I want to be the hero in this journey
and know that I did a good job in this life.
I want to have mastered my skills.
By the time its over for me,
I will have been all used up
like guitar strings that have been played
over and again until rusted copper.

I want to live a life where I enjoy my youth
and have it too.
I want to live with such gratitude
So that by the time I'm ready
to leave this world, I will sense
not much left but ardor
for the next adventure.

-Christy Cosper

About Christy Cosper

Christy Cosper is a Licensed Marriage and Family Therapist, Certified Sex Addiction Therapist, and an AAMFT approved clinical supervisor. Christy has extensive experience in the field of Addictive Disorders along with other Mental Health Disorders. She is also a relationship expert, specializing in the restoration of relationships with chronic discord. Christy has been working as a clinician in a private practice setting since 2007. In addition to clinical work, Christy also leads intensive weekend workshops and hosts educational and spiritual retreats that focus on healing and improving relationship with self. Her practice includes a wide range of services such as: individual therapy; couples therapy; family therapy; group therapy for men, women and partners; mindfulness-based relapse prevention; recovery coaching; partner coaching; and psycho-education services.

Christy holds a Bachelors Degree in Psychology with a minor in addictive disorders; a Masters Degree in Clinical Psychology with an emphasis in Marriage and Family Therapy and she is currently a PhD candidate at Oregon State University specializing in Counselor-Education.

Christy resides in Long Beach, California

Made in the USA
Monee, IL
16 May 2024

58535848R00188